FUN WITH YOUR MICROSCOPE

A microscope outfit intended for amateur use. It comes sup
plied with stains, slides, specimens, and accessory equipment.

FUN
WITH YOUR
MICROSCOPE

by

RAYMOND F. YATES

APPLETON-CENTURY-CROFTS, INC.
New York

To
the memory
of my brother
ARTHUR JAMES YATES
1883-1942

Contents

Contents

Photographs

ix

1

Your Microscope

THE full-fledged amateur microscopist knows his instrument. Indeed, if he is a cautious person and wishes to spend his money wisely, he will familiarize himself with the details of microscope construction and operation before he makes his investment. Thus will he be able properly to appraise the various refinements and accessories and on the whole make a more intelligent purchase. An introduction to the mechanics and optics of a microscope also makes for quicker mastery of the instrument.

Before we can hope to understand microscopic or optical magnification, we must first learn something about the physics of light and especially something about what we might call the "light-benders." Really, the light-benders are quite easily understood. Anything that transmits or permits the passage of light must, by the very nature of things, be a light-bender. Among these things, of course, such materials as glass and quartz stand out, but there are also celluloid, the various transparent and translucent minerals, waxed paper, water, etc. We, however, do not need to carry our investigation beyond glass, and we shall start our examination of the subject with the behavior of a beam of light as it passes through various glass shapes.

Although it is not absolutely pertinent to the subject at hand, it may be said that nothing matches the speed of light in a vacuum, which is 186,000 miles per second. What is more important for us to know is that the speed of light is not constant but depends upon the nature of the medium through which it may be traveling. It has a certain speed for passing through glass, water, etc. In every instance, the speed of light is reduced as compared with its speed through a vacuum. The reduction is not great, but it can be measured, and, what is more important to the amateur microscopist, the reduction in speed entails phenomena upon which microscopy is based.

Perhaps we shall be assisted by turning our attention to Fig. 1. Here is shown the behavior of a beam of light passing through the air and into a piece of glass. Upon entering the glass, the beam is bent as a result of its being slowed. The degree of bending will depend upon the nature and composition of the glass. We do not have the space here to enter into a discussion of why the light is bent, but we can take it for granted that it is and that, furthermore, the *degree* of bending is different for all materials through which light is capable of passing. Indeed, physicists have devised a special instrument for measuring the degree of deflection: it is called a refractometer, after the word refraction. Light bent by passage through water, glass, etc., is said to be refracted, and the degree of refraction is referred to as the "refractive index." Thus every material through which a beam of light can be forced has its own refractive index.

Referring once more to Fig. 1, we note with interest that upon emerging from the glass the beam of light resumes its normal course; it is really bent again. But here we must keep in mind that the surface of glass where the light enters is perfectly parallel to the surface where the light leaves. In short, the

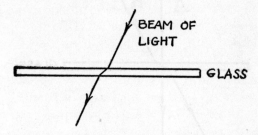

FIG. 1. A beam of light is bent when it strikes the surface of glass, but, after passing through, it resumes its original direction.

top and bottom of the glass are the same. Should one be at an angle different from the other, the light would behave differently. But more of this later. What we wish to do for the moment is to become impressed with the fact that light is knocked out of its normal path through air or through a vacuum when it encounters another medium through which it is capable of passing.

There is still another thing about this matter of bending or refraction that demands attention on the part of the ambitious microscopist who wishes to master the fundamentals of this fascinating subject.

We must bring into our calculations the angle at which the beam of light strikes the top surface of the glass. This is called the "angle of incidence," and, if we refer to A and B, Fig. 2, we shall have little difficulty in understanding this important part of our topic. It is to be noted that at A, there is no bending of light. However, when the light beam strikes the

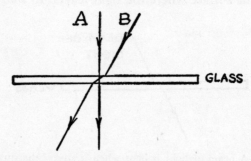

FIG. 2. Showing that the angle of incidence determines the degree of refraction. The beam A, striking at right angles (90°) to the surface of the glass, is not bent at all.

glass at an angle either to the right or to the left of the beam at A, bending will occur, and this bending will follow the degree of incidence. The greater the angle of incidence the greater the degree of bending.

It is this peculiar property of light that provides us with the miracle of magnification. If light was not bent upon passing through glass or other equally clear substances, then there would be no microscopes or magnifying glasses, and the progress of the world would have been arrested in no small measure. Many of our great discoveries—especially in medicine, metallurgy, botany, and chemistry—have been made possible only by the aid of optical magnification.

Although there is a wide variety of lenses and highly specialized optical shapes for light bending, the diagram in Fig. 3 outlines all the more commonly employed lenses. Some are used in microscopes, some are not. And, of course, microscopes vary greatly in design and construction: some are simple and cheap;

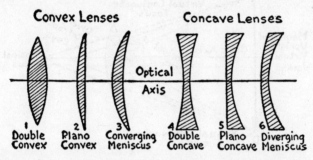

Convex Lenses   **Concave Lenses**

Optical

Axis

1 Double Convex   2 Plano Convex   3 Converging Meniscus   4 Double Concave   5 Plano Concave   6 Diverging Meniscus

FIG. 3. Common lenses ranging from convex to concave. Several of these are employed in the more expensive microscopes.

others are involved and expensive, with a highly complicated lens system designed to conserve light and eliminate as far as is humanly possible the distortion of the image due to imperfection in the glass and its ground surfaces.

From the series of common lens shapes illustrated in Fig. 3, we shall select the double convex type for a more thorough examination, since it is in this form more than in any other that glass blossoms forth in the shining new microscope to bring endless wonders and entertainment to its fortunate owner. Before passing on to this new matter, however, it might be advisable to glance back once more at Fig. 3 and note that lenses may be divided into two general groups, convex and concave. Combinations of the two forms are used for special duties.

For the present, of course, we are not so much interested in lenses as such as we are in their effect on

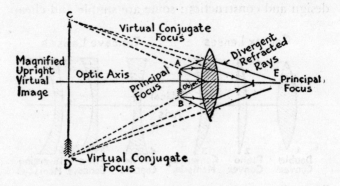

The Formation of a Virtual Image

FIG. 4. The optical properties of a double convex lens, the principal lens of the microscope. Here will be seen the generation of the actual image in comparison with the magnified or "virtual image."

the light which passes through them. This is particularly true of the double convex light-bender that functions so importantly in even the cheapest microscopes.

The sketch, Fig. 4, will permit us to understand some of the fundamental optical properties of such lenses. It will pay us to stop long enough to digest the essentials. Upon completing our chore here, we turn

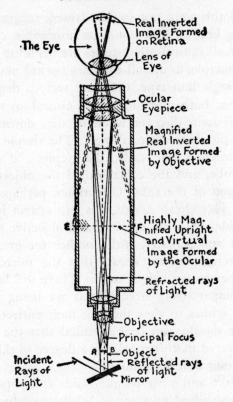

Real Inverted
Image Formed
on Retina

The Eye

Lens of
Eye

Ocular
Eyepiece

Magnified
Real Inverted
Image Formed
by Objective

Highly Mag-
nified Upright
and Virtual
Image Formed
by the Ocular

Refracted rays
of Light

Objective

Principal Focus

Object
Reflected rays
of light
Mirror

Incident
Rays of
Light

FIG. 5. The position E in the diagram marks the virtual image in a microscope. We also see here the lens arrangement used in the more expensive instruments.

to Fig. 5, where the optical principle of the simple compound microscope is laid down diagrammatically in as simple a manner as possible. We note that the secret of optical magnification lies not only in the peculiar properties of lenses but in the human eye itself. If this were not so constituted, magnification with any kind of lens would be impossible.

While all optical microscopes are made up on the same principle, as are all ordinary optical magnifiers of the single lens type, there are various degrees of refinement both mechanical and optical, as the student will soon discover when he digs down in his jeans to purchase an instrument. The simple 'scopes have two lenses, one, called the eyepiece, at the top of the tube, and the other, called the objective, at the bottom of the tube. Oftentimes, perhaps in all save the very cheap device, this lens system is interchangeable; both the eyepiece and objective may be removed and replaced with another for greater or less power. It is not always that the microscopist wishes the greatest magnification. There will be times when comparatively large objects are being viewed and one wishes to view them in their entirety. The beginner should also bear in mind that the costly, high-powered machines call for a degree of skill that takes a long time to acquire.

In Figs. 6 and 7, we see the inside and outside details of a standard microscope. While the type shown may lie beyond both the pocket-book and the skill of the beginner, it does nevertheless correspond in many ways to the simple amateur machines and for that reason it is used as an example. Its main difference lies in refinements, largely mechanical. Naturally, its optical equipment is superior, its lenses being more carefully ground and corrected.

Even the cheapest microscopes involve two metal

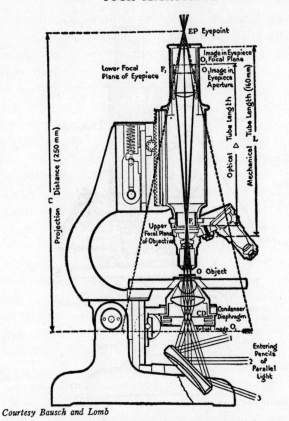

Courtesy Bausch and Lomb

FIG. 6. A careful study of this diagram will acquaint the novice with all the essential features of good microscope construction.

tubes, one sliding or telescoping within the other. Were it not for this adjustable feature, it would be impossible to focus. Of course, in the cheaper 'scopes (two to five dollars) this adjustment is usually brought about by pushing or pulling the smaller

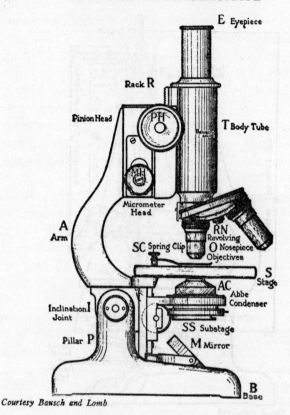

E Eyepiece

Rack R

Pinion Head

PH

T Body Tube

MH

Micrometer
Head

A
Arm

SC Spring Clip

RN
Revolving
O Nosepiece
Objectives

S
Stage

AC
Abbe
Condenser

Inclination I
Joint

SS Substage

Pillar P

M Mirror

B
Base

Courtesy Bausch and Lomb

FIG. 7. The names of the various parts of a complete microscope such as may be found in professional use.

(and upper) tube in and out of the larger one. This,
however, is a pretty crude form of adjustment even
though it serves where magnification is comparatively
low (more will be said about magnification later).

Indeed, where high power is used, such adjustment

is hopelessly crude because of the highly critical placement of the lens system that becomes necessary. In extreme cases, the movement of a thousandth of an inch will destroy the focus.

Returning to Fig. 7, we note that the big tube is called the body tube and the smaller one the eyepiece tube. Attached to the outside of the body tube, we discover a gear rack (R) and meshing with this is a pinion gear controlled by the knob (PH). In the case of a high-powered instrument, however, even this rack-and-pinion control is not sufficiently sensitive for great magnification. Thus, located just below the knob for this rough adjustment, we find a second knob, controlling a micrometer adjustment which is extremely fine and accurate. This is a refinement that is found on machines selling for $100 or more.

The modest amateur microscope is usually provided with a single objective of definite power. In a few cases, the more elaborate 'scopes come provided with a second objective that can be screwed into place over the first one to increase the power of magnification. We note that, in the case of the more expensive instruments, as shown in Figs. 6 and 7, several (usually three) objectives of different degrees of power are arranged on a revolving member, and that it is possible to snap any one of these into position very quickly. This is a nice refinement, but it amounts to a matter of convenience only, and the amateur certainly has little cause to lament the absence of such a contraption on his machine. It saves time for the professional worker, but it is a great luxury for the hobbyist.

Directing our attention for the moment to Fig. 6, we note that light strikes an adjustable mirror underneath the stage of the instrument. From this point it is reflected upward through the lens system. Here, however, we have another refinement, called a condenser, that is not found on cheaper instruments. When great magnification is used (greater by far than we can hope to afford or conquer as amateurs), the distribution and full use of all available light becomes a matter of high importance, and it is the function of the condenser to gather in the light and to conserve it as far as possible for use on the object. The wisdom of such an arrangement becomes obvious when it is realized that as an object is magnified, the light that it reflects becomes weaker and weaker. For instance, if it is magnified 2,000 times the light it reflects will be proportionately fainter. Of course, with our modest little amateur machines where magnification amounts to a small fraction of this figure, the matter of conserving light is not quite so important.

Although it is not shown on the drawings of the instrument illustrated in Figs. 6 and 7, high-powered, expensive microscopes also come equipped with mechanical devices to be used in shifting the objective. It should be observed that, in the case of high-powered magnification, only a very small area of any object can be seen or inspected at one time. Exploration even of some of the larger bacteria calls for movement and shifting. Here the fingers are entirely inadequate. Our coördination of muscles is far too crude for such things. When a magnification of 2,000 times is being employed, a displacement of 1/5000 of an inch at a time is necessary in exploring an object. Hence, the need for micrometric equipment. Thus, with devices that permit the professional to raise or lower his tube 1/10,000 of an inch at a time and to move his object in any one of four directions 1/5000 of an inch at a time, he is in a fine position to do excellent work.

Before purchasing an instrument, it is important that the beginner understand something about magnifying power and the method used in rating it. After all, amateur or professional, what one is purchasing is magnifying power. And curiously enough, magnification can be good or bad. This will probably sound strange to the would-be hobbyist until he happens to recall that a camera, no matter how costly its case, refinement, or finish, can be no better than its lens. We should resolve not to be taken in by claims of high magnification coming at low cost. High magnification may be had at low cost, but because of the unavoidable distortion of badly ground lenses, this magnification is pretty useless. The honest manufacturer attempts to give the amateur a degree of magnification that will not only come within his skill of manipulation but that will also deliver up an image as close to the original as possible. Therefore the beginner should not be available for loud claims when he makes his purchase, and he would also do well to make his choice among the products of the several well-known optical houses supplying this sort of equipment.

Naturally, the amateur will be limited in his purchases not only by his money but also by his skill. The person who, without previous experience, marches forth and purchases a high-powered, $200 machine is being pretty thoughtless and even silly. He will not have the technical ability to enjoy his purchase, and the chances are that he will find himself unable to master manipulation before his enthusiasm expires.

Prices for amateur equipment range all the way from $2.50 to $50. Excellent pieces made by the larger manufacturers of optical equipment may be had at a price in the neighborhood of $20. If the beginner can possibly afford it, he should purchase one of these instruments rather than a cheaper one boasting equal magnification. He may have to save his money a little longer, but it will be worth it. Should it be necessary because of financial stringencies to remain in the five-dollar zone, then a certain amount of distortion must be expected. But even here a lot of fun may be had and a lot of things be done. Perhaps the hobbyist may slake his thirst with such a modest instrument and save his pennies for something better while he is learning to use it.

Not a small number of beginners are seized with the notion of making a second-hand purchase. This may be a good idea if certain precautions are followed. First, a reliable dealer should be sought out and a guarantee against defect should be had with the purchase. Second, the beginner should make sure that the lens supplied with the instrument is not scratched in any way, even microscopically. Third, he should still hold his purchase to a comparatively simple machine, perhaps of the type used for high-school biology classes. Many of these instruments come equipped with two objectives, and they are fine pieces. What is more, the manufacturers of such microscopes often take large numbers of them in from colleges in part payment for newer equipment. These instruments are then sent back into the factory for refinishing and repair and are finally offered to the public for less than one-half their original price. Should the beginner be able to handle such a purchase financially ($25 to $45), it is to be advised. Most of these instruments are built in such a way as to be available for many attachments and refinements that the hobbyist can acquire gradually as his skill increases.

So much for an elementary examination of microscopes and their purchase. We shall in all probability be impatient to get on to the more practical aspects of our subject, especially as they relate to actual manipulation. One certainly can not be blamed for such impatience.

However, before we pass on to the next chapter, it might be well to have a final word about lenses. The designation "compound microscope" is used to distinguish the average microscope from the ordinary magnifying glass, which, no matter how we look at it, is also a microscope. The compound machine such as we shall be using has a multi-lens optical system, the optical value of which is not limited to the largeness of the images employed but is extended to provide clearness or absence of distortion. This is a combination of factors appreciated only by the experienced worker.

Magnification in the case of a compound microscope may be adjusted in three ways. The length of the microscopic tube may be increased or decreased; higher- or lower-powered oculars or eyepieces may be employed; or higher- or lower-powered objectives may be employed.

Again we warn the prospective purchaser not to buy a nondescript microscope on the basis of its magnifying power alone. Such a purchase may turn out to be utterly worthless. Employing such an instrument at the peak of its magnifying power, one might not know just what one was looking at, so bad could the distortion be.

All this boils down to what the expert microscopist calls resolution. For our purpose we may put resolution down as the ability to minimize distortion as the magnification is increased. It is a matter concerned with the best forms of optical glass and the expert shaping and polishing of the lens made from the glass. There can be no substitute for careful, expert workmanship.

To arrive at the maximum power of an instrument, which is usually labeled by its manufacturer, we may multiply the power of magnification of the eyepiece or ocular by that of the objective. For instance, we find 10x marked on the ocular. This means that it will magnify an object ten times. If, in turn, that object is again magnified ten times by the objective lens (also marked 10x), then the ultimate power of such a 'scope would be a mere matter of 10 $\times$ 10 or 100x.

Professionals require a number of data with their lenses when they purchase them. All the optical characteristics are included, such as focal length, power, color correction, aperture, etc. Although a color-corrected lens is nice to have, such luxuries are usually beyond the amateur.

2

First Lessons

THE degree of fun and revelation to be had with a microscope will be determined not so much by the optical power of the instrument at hand as by the ability and skill of the hobbyist to operate it. Should a beginner attempt his first exploits with an expensive microscope of vast optical range and use it at the peak of its power, he would, unless favored by great tenacity and patience, soon tire of his new-found pleasures and turn to a more productive hobby.

This statement is not meant in any way to frighten the would-be microscopist, but it is meant to warn him. Even a child can manipulate the low-powered instrument, but the extreme limits of magnification call for a form of skill that is slowly acquired, and one can not be expected to vault the difficulties in a few hours. What is more, there is a vast and interesting sub-world of nature that may be adequately viewed with comparatively low magnification, a world so vast, indeed, that even though we lived to be a thousand years old we could never fully explore it. This world is both organic and inorganic, living and dead, and we unwittingly scuff many of its marvelous specimens under our feet.

If there is any early advice to be given to the beginner, it is not to be too ambitious. We must proceed cautiously, learn as we go along, and not expect to see everything in a single evening. Should a microscope be provided with high- and low-powered objectives, we should elect to use the low-powered piece until we can be sure that we have mastered manipulation sufficiently to warrant advancement. Ordinarily, unless we are unduly impatient, we shall find enough entertainment in the lower ranges to last us for many months. During this time we may acquire proficiency in mastering our 'scope.

Before we delve into the mechanical operation of a microscope, we shall pause a moment and consider what we may call the "hygiene" of the optical system. Stupidity and carelessness in keeping these clean have cost many an amateur one or more lenses. We should therefore heed advice relating to this vital department of our new hobby.

First, in handling any lens intended for magnification, we must guard against scratches. By this we do not necessarily refer to big scratches that one may see with the naked eye. A microscope lens may be disastrously damaged in this way without our being able to detect the disaster with the eye unaided. The lens of any microscope must be handled with the greatest of care. Dropping is fatal more often than not, and even the choice of materials for cleaning must be made with care. For instance, if one used a piece of linen with grain alcohol to clean a lens and a single piece of grit was not noticed, a cruel series of scratches would undoubtedly result. This might not be noticed until the microscope was used again.

Scratches resulting from this sort of cleaning can be avoided by the gentle brushing or wiping of the lens with clean, alcohol-soaked linen. No matter what medium is used for cleaning the lens, no pressure should be applied to the surface.

The use of the special soft tissues sold in the optical stores should not be overlooked. They are inexpensive and safe, if we take care to see that the box holding them is kept closed and free from dust. Every piece used should first be examined for dust particles. Grain alcohol may be used as the fluid. It is less expensive than the special preparations.

The hobbyist must remain ever mindful that he is in a new world, the world of very small things. Trifles are magnified as well as objects. Mole-hills really do turn into mountains. Little things begin to count. For instance, we might not give sufficient heed to the warning to keep our fingers off our lenses. The oils of the skin are quickly transferred to clean glass surfaces and, once there, are difficult to remove completely *even with alcohol*. One is likely to forget that oil is merely diluted when dissolved in alcohol and that we may wind up our lens cleaning with a thin film still left on the lens. Thereafter, microscopic dust particles will tend to adhere to such smeared surfaces.

Contrary to what might be expected, chamois, even

the best, should be strictly avoided in the cleaning of lenses. Like all animal skins, it holds a certain amount of animal oil, and its process of preparation does not remove all of it. Enough remains to cause trouble by spreading a fine film over glass surfaces that have been rubbed with it. The fact that we can not see such deposits does not mean that they are not there.

Another precept to be borne in mind is that, once our lens has been cleaned, we should take as much care as possible to keep it clean. This means that the microscope must be kept covered either in its own case or under glass. Cloth covers, because of their tendency not only to pass dust but to hold it, should not be used. The hobbyist will find that a wide-mouthed quart fruit-jar will serve nicely with the smaller instruments. Larger microscopes can be covered with a gallon glass jug from which the bottom has been removed by any of the approved methods of cutting glass.

We are now ready to turn to the matter of operation. Even the beginner will realize that light and the illumination of objects must be a very important function. The good amateur microscopist must become quite expert in arranging such matters. In this respect he is something like the amateur photographer with a good camera and no knowledge of proper lighting: good cameras are of little use under such conditions. Whether or not an object can be seen clearly will depend largely upon the microscopist's source of light and his skill in arranging it. This subject is being discussed now because all lessons in the actual mechanical manipulation of microscopes must be predicated upon the assumption that good illumination is at hand. Illumination must amount to a compromise between eyestrain and the adequate lighting of the object. We learn that there can be too much as well as too little light. The uniform distribution of light also is a matter of importance.

Natural illumination is difficult to beat. This is to be found at a well-lighted window. A small concave mirror arranged on gimbals is mounted beneath the stage of every microscope. It is the function of this small mirror to gather light, concentrate it, and reflect it upward through the object. Should the object be so dense as to demand a more powerful source of illumination, the observer must turn to electric sources. But more of that later. Most ordinary specimens can be adequately examined by means of daylight coming in an uncovered window.

The adjustment of the mirror is simple enough. The observer merely puts the object or specimen in place, peeps through the eyepiece, and adjusts the mirror until a clear, even illumination results. If the object is especially transparent, it may be that too much light will reach the eye. Should this happen, the position of the mirror is shifted a bit to reduce the quantity of the light. After a little experience with the mirror and this sort of observation, the hobbyist will find quick and adequate adjustment quite easy.

Up to the present time, we have considered only

the transparent object or specimen. Not all the things we shall want to look at with our microscope are transparent. Some of them will be opaque or unable to pass light. Obviously, such specimens must be examined by means of light reflected from their surfaces. Minerals fall into this class of specimens, as well as many other interesting sources of study. When amateur microscopes of low power are employed for the examination of such surfaces, there will be little or no trouble in arranging the lighting.

Most instruments are equipped for such work as far as the mirror is concerned. This may be shifted from beneath the stage to a position above it, so that light is reflected downward upon an object. Of course, where rough surfaces are being examined, one must avoid shadows. With illumination coming from one side only, this might be difficult. In the case of minerals having rough surfaces, the difficulty can be overcome by grinding the surface flat on a wheel. It must be clear also that artificial light may be used for the examination of opaque objects.

Inasmuch as a great deal of time with our hobby will be spent during evenings, some sort of inexpensive but adequate source of light must be established for work during these hours. Here we must not feel that the more light the better, because for the sort of program we have in mind this is not by any means true. We shall want just a little light of the right kind—not over five or six candle-power.

Our attention is directed to Fig. 8, where the details of a small illuminator are given. Such equipment may be purchased, but there is little need for this even for those with few tools.

The mechanical details of the device are so simple that the drawing should prove entirely adequate in

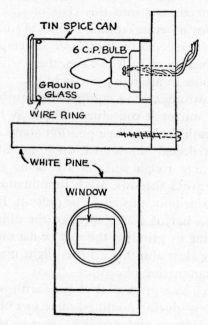

FIG. 8. Details for the construction of a simple microscope illuminator.

supplying information. The builder may take liberties with the design shown except for the ground glass. This must be used to diffuse the light. The illuminator will be practically useless without it. To keep the device small and workmanlike, a miniature

110-volt bulb is used. These may be had at the electrical counters of most chain stores, and they cost only a few pennies each. Oftentimes sockets of the correct size may also be had for such bulbs. Should the sockets not be available, the bulb may be mounted as shown in the drawing and the two connections soldered in place. These bulbs have a considerable life, so the need for soldering connections in place each time there is a burn-out will not be too troublesome.

Light is a big subject in microscopy, and we should not feel that everything about it has been said. Indeed, we have barely touched on the matter especially as it relates to the more technical side of the art. However, enough has been said to give a sane grasp of the subject and if we take heed we shall be able to do very nicely for ourselves. Here experience counts more than any other method of instruction.

The remainder of our chapter will be devoted to the manipulation of the microscope itself. This may sound a lot easier than it actually is, but still there is no need to fear the subject. Respect is quite enough. We simply want to guard against being too ambitious "all of a sudden." We should resolve to achieve a slowly and thoroughly acquired skill. Such skill will perpetuate our interest and pleasure for many years.

Assuming that the ownership of an expensive, high-powered instrument will be rare among our readers, our data concerning manipulation will be limited to the operation of simple machines, ranging upward in cost from $5 or so to a top of $25.

To insure comfort, we should first make sure that the table or bench used to hold the microscope is not too high or too low and that, above all, we are not going to be forced into an awkward or unnatural position. This is a prime requirement that can not be overemphasized. Obviously, the height of the bench or table used must depend somewhat on the angular dimensions of the party involved. Hence, no definite measurements can be given.

Assuming that a comfortable position has been established and that we have adequate light of the right kind at our disposal, we proceed to the first lesson in focusing. Here we aim principally at getting the *feel* of the microscope. Perhaps we shall have cause to be surprised.

We may use for specimens a number of things about the household, provided we have two glass slides of the type that come with most microscope kits. In any case, we must first recognize the importance of *flatness* and *thinness*. When transparent specimens are being viewed, both flatness and thinness are essential. With opaque objects, flatness is quite enough. Here it is well to bear in mind that because of the great magnification involved, a tiny speck no more than a few thousandths of an inch in height may turn out optically to assume the proportions of Mount Everest. If we focus at the base of the speck, the top will become nothing but a shapeless and meaningless blur.

Either a hair or a small piece of onion skin may be useful as a first specimen. Let us assume that a hair has been pressed between two microscope slides and that this will be our first venture "at the wheel." We slip the slides under the holding clips, endeavoring to bring the hair itself as close to the exact center of the stage as possible, so that it will be directly under the objective lens—which, by the way, is very small. We assume that the light has been focused by means of the mirror and that a nice, even field of illumination has been established.

Grasping the focusing knob, we at the same time peer into the eyepiece. The chances are many to one that we shall see nothing. But where is the hair? It is still there! Perhaps it is not in position. We decide to move it a bit. This is done. Still nothing happens. We see nothing, not even a blur. We move the slide in all directions and there is still no image. Has it occurred to us to turn the focusing knob? We try that. Still no results. Figuring that a hair is pretty small, we decide to bring the instrument to a rough focus with something easier to find. A piece of tissue paper is now slipped in place and, with one eye away from the eyepiece and with both eyes on the objective of the miscroscope, we turn the focusing knob until the objective lens at the lower end of the tube is within a quarter of an inch or so of the surface of the glass microscope slide. Great care must be exercised in seeing that the objective does not touch the slide. Damage is apt to result if it does. Still greater damage can result, even up to the point of breaking the objective lens, if, without looking, we carelessly adjust the focusing tube downward until it contacts the slide. As we gain in experience, our focusing will come fast and easy, but we must make sure at first that we are not going to ruin part of our equipment. Replacing a broken objective lens would mean a considerable percentage of the total cost of the whole instrument.

Having placed the objective close to the surface of the slide under which the tissue paper rests, we now return to the eyepiece and peek through. Certainly we now know that our specimen will be centered, even if it is not in focus. Slowly, we turn the focusing knob in the direction needed to raise the focusing tube and objective lens. Presto! The fibers making up the tissue paper finally come into clear view, and we note how sensitive the focus is even to a slight movement of the focusing knob. A movement slightly upward or downward is sufficient to throw the whole scene into meaningless blurs. It might be well to spend a few moments moving the lens tube up and down just to get the feel of focusing.

We return to the hair full of the conviction that we shall conquer it! However, we have made sure that we are going to be somewhere near the focus of that hair by leaving our objective undisturbed. Thus, when the tissue paper is replaced with the hair, we should be somewhere near the proper focus. This is a roundabout way and not recommended to any but the rank beginner. However, it does help and it does impress us with the need for experience in our work. Soon the worker will laugh at his early efforts to find tiny things and bring them in focus.

When the hair is set back on the stage, the focus should not be touched. Rather, we glue our eye to the eyepiece, and, with either one or two hands, we *slowly* move the slide about, keeping our eagle eye open for the elusive hair. Quite suddenly we see something, heaven only knows what, sweeping past our vision at a terrific pace. It could be anything, but it happens to be the hair. Of course, the beginner will wonder why it moved so *fast* and so *far* when he was being so careful in moving it slowly and over a short distance. The answer to that can easily be guessed even by the novice if he will give it a little thought. Certainly it must be clear that distance and speed are magnified, in addition to the dimensions. Indeed, it is this that gives the beginner so much trouble. When extreme powers are used, as with the more expensive instruments, special mechanism is often employed by the professionals to move specimens a short distance at a time and under conditions of perfect control. Thus may the surface of a tiny, highly magnified article be progressively explored. Another thing that the amateur fails to understand is that, even at the lower power of say, 250 to 300 diameters, only a very small area comes into view at one time. With a high-powered instrument, some time would be required to explore thoroughly an area as small as $\frac{1}{8}$ inch square. These things should be fixed in mind. They will help us understand our problem better, and skill comes through understanding.

The modestly priced little microscopes of the type that most of us will be using have a coarse adjustment made with the knurled knob, and they also have a finer (vernier) adjustment, usually on the stage, to raise and lower it slowly. Such a refinement is needed in connection with the examination of most objects. It permits hair-like adjustment which will be found quite necessary at times. The adjustment is not micrometric as it must be on the more powerful instruments but it is entirely adequate for the degree of magnification made possible.

In reviewing the matter of focusing for beginners, emphasis should be laid on the danger of our becoming too ambitious; too anxious to skip or gloss over the little experiences that every good technician must go through. Thus, if our instrument comes supplied to us with two objectives, one for low and one for higher powered magnification, we should start things off with the low-powered instrument, and we should make very sure that we have mastered this as best we can before we pass on to the bigger objects and the higher magnification. This is sound advice, and it should not be passed off too lightly. Another thing: the beginner should be extremely careful about jamming the objective lens down tightly on a slide resting on the stage. This often damages the lens and sometimes breaks it. If the right start is made with the objective lens close to the slide, then *focusing up* follows.

Those who have never before manipulated a microscope are usually badly confused and even frustrated to a degree during the first hour or so. However, once we succeed in really "bagging" an image, confidence gradually forms. It has been said before that both speed and size are magnified. Add to this the fact that motion, as well as the image, is *reversed,* and one can easily understand some of the difficulties of bringing a small specimen to rest in the center of the field where it belongs.

The use of the lower-powered objective does not need to set us down in the kindergarten of the school for microscopists. The professionals also make good use of low-powered examination when certain specimens are to be viewed, especially the larger ones. The lower power gives them a better all-around view, and preliminary work is often done with such equipment. Therefore, we should not by any means become seized with the notion that low magnification is intended only for the novice. Should the use of low power reveal some particularly interesting part of a specimen, and should the worker then wish to make a more careful exploration of that part or area, he turns to his more powerful optical equipment. Naturally, the specimen must again be brought into focus after the lens replacement has been made.

It might be advisable at this point to pass on a word or two to tinkerers, and especially the type that has an insatiable desire to see what makes the wheels go around. Microscopes, especially the good ones, should not be tampered with any more than is necessary. This is especially true concerning the micrometer or fine adjustment. Once this is disassembled, a tinkerer might have cause to regret his curiosity.

Much more could be said about the operation of

an instrument, but it is also true that the best way to learn is by experience rather than by words. The fundamentals have been set forth, and we should be ready to take our first exciting peep at the biggest of all possible worlds: the world ordinarily too small to see.

3

Ten-Cent Microscope

WATER, being transparent, also falls in the class of light-benders. When a beam of light passes through water it will bend to a degree depending upon its degree of incidence. It should follow, then, that the optical properties of water are in general very much like optical properties of glass. This is indeed quite true, and if water could be made to assume the form of a lens, the lens would perform almost the same way as its counterpart in glass.

While it would be most difficult if not impossible to hold a large mass of water in a definite shape, small bodies of water, due to the phenomenon of surface tension, aided by gravity, assume spherical shapes. Raindrops are almost spherical and, even though they are not perfectly formed, they bear optical properties that make them powerful magnifiers under certain conditions. By the simple expedient of dropping a single drop of water from a medicine dropper, we can set up a magnifier of no mean power. Although the power of water-drop lenses varies with the size and the shape of the drop, magnification will average somewhere in the neighborhood of 100 diameters.

By exercising a little ingenuity we can build a frame upon which to mount our water-drop lens and also to reflect light through it so that we may see in the approved fashion. At 100 diameters one may look at many marvels that are far beyond the range of the unaided eye.

At the outset, it may be said that neither the materials nor the dimensions of our water-drop microscope are critical or vital. Steel or copper are just as good as brass, and a thin piece of plywood will serve almost as well as the masonite recommended for the stage.

To begin, let us carefully examine the photograph of the finished instrument. First there is the lens. This is "mounted" in a pin-hole punched in the thin sheet-metal strip at the top of the instrument. Directly underneath this will be found the stage upon which the glass slide carrying the specimen is mounted. This stage is carried by a metal tube which can be slid up and down in the wooden frame: this is for the purpose of focusing the device. Light is reflected upward from a small mirror below. The beam passes through the brass tube carrying the stage on up through the specimen and the "lens." A microscope of this sort may be put together in a few hours, and it will afford countless hours of fun. Of course, the "lens" eventually evaporates, but plenty more may be had from the kitchen faucet.

The frame of the instrument is so simply made that there is little need of wasting words on its construction and assembly. A word or two about the stage, however, may not come amiss. It will be noticed that the brass tube is forced into the hole of the masonite piece. To a novice, that may sound much easier to do than it actually is. The chances are that the builder will not have just the right sized drill to produce a forced fit between the hole and the piece of metal tubing. Therefore, it is better to use a drill smaller than the outside diameter of the tubing and carefully to file it larger with a round file. When the right size is reached, the tube may be forced home with a hammer. Care should be taken to stop filing when the hole is just less in diameter than the outside diameter of the tube. Of course, it is also possible to use a piece of heavy sheet brass for the stage, in which case the metal tube might be soldered to the stage.

A hole must also be drilled in the cross member of the frame, and the tube must have a sliding fit in this. Here, too, the builder should drill an undersized hole for the tube and then carefully make it larger by the aid of a small round wood rasp or a round coarse file. The tube should fit in this hole tightly enough so that it will remain in any position in which it is placed. Otherwise our little microscope will not remain in focus.

Perhaps a word or two about the mirror and its mounting will help. Here we must forego the luxury of a concave mirror which gathers more light, but a piece of perfectly flat mirror will nevertheless aid powerfully in our work. This is glued to a heavy block of wood, and the block is mounted on a wire

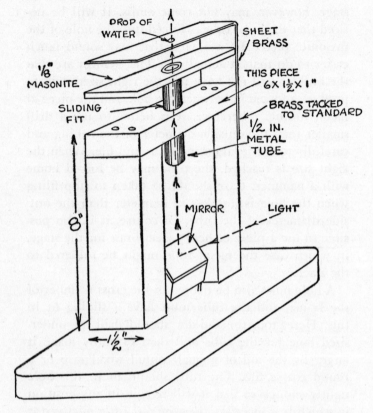

FIG. 9. The constructional details of the water-drop microscope.

swivel. The holes drilled in the sides of the block should be slightly smaller than the wire used. Otherwise, the mirror will not remain in the position in which it is placed.

The next operation is that of punching the hole in

the piece of metal serving as the "lens" mounting or holder. This may be done with a prick punch or, barring that, a small nail that has been filed or ground to needle-like sharpness. The hole should not be smaller than 1/32 or larger than 1/16 of an inch in diameter. The novice should also plan on spoiling several pieces of metal before a good job is done. The punching should be done over a piece of hard wood, and the worker should take care to remove the burr with a small fine file. It might be advisable to make five or six of these pieces while we are about it and to try each one with a drop of water to determine which of the holes made turns out to be the best and which one offers the largest, clearest image. After this determination has been made, the piece may be permanently fixed in place.

After the instrument has been assembled, we can not expect to obtain perfect results instantly. Here, too, some skill must be developed, and this will come only with experience. For instance, there is a distinct relationship between the size of the hole and the size of the drop of water placed over it. The smaller the drop of water, the greater the degree of magnification, but we are faced with practical limitations concerning the smallness of the drop. Aided by a medicine dropper we experiment with drops of water, noting each time how large and how clear the image is. Perhaps we shall need an evening or two for this preliminary investigation, but that will be a small price to pay for the fun that can be had with this simple equipment.

It will be part of our experience to learn that when the microscope is used for a long time, the drop of water gradually evaporates. The rate of evaporation will depend entirely upon the condition of the atmosphere. On humid days, the rate will be very slow.

There is a lot to be learned with a little instrument of this sort, especially for the persevering fellow who will devote enough time to completely mastering the technic. Many of the specimens described in the following chapter are available for examination by this method.

4

Specimens: Where and How to Find Them

OUR hunt for specimens does not need to carry us far afield. Many interesting things can be found about the house in winter or summer. Indeed, the whole world teems with grist for our mill, and no matter how long our enthusiasm lasts for our hobby, we shall never run out of things to look for and marvel at. The world of the infinitely small is infinitely large, and perhaps the most majestic part of creation lies beyond the bounds of ordinary sight.

We shall be so impatient to set out upon our first adventures that we shall in all probability want to seek out our first few objects as quickly as possible, in the house. This can be done easily enough, but here let us make a note that not all specimens are instantly available for examination. Part of the skill that we shall be called upon to develop will have to do with the preparation of things to look at. We can not expect that all and sundry things may be chucked under the objective lens and that they will reveal their innermost optical secrets without further ado. Part of our fun will come in preparing specimens, many of them permanently, building up what we might call our Album of Wonders, permanent mountings made between glass.

Returning to the subject of immediately available specimens, it is to be recalled that the whole vegetable kingdom abounds with such material for quick, preliminary investigation. Most leaves and flower petals, for instance, will pass enough light for quick examination. Of course, the more light they pass the better, and the more we shall see. It will be necessary to keep the petals and leaves as flat as possible while they are being examined, and this calls for pressing them between two microscope slides during examination.

We shall have much more to say about microscope slides later on. In the meantime, it is assumed that the beginner either has had a few of them supplied with his outfit or has purchased a few from a supply house. If this assumption is wrong, then the would-be microscopist should see to it that a small stock of such slides is laid in. Fortunately, they are not expensive, and any substitutes that we might obtain would probably be inadequate. The optical purity of glass is an important factor with us. We need glass that will not only pass as much light as possible but also glass that will not distort our images. All of us have noticed the distortion brought about by ordinary window-glass. One can well imagine that this would be greatly increased with magnification. Another factor is that the little microscope glasses not only are exceptionally clear but also come with nicely ground edges.

Should we be seized with an attack of microscopy

during the wintertime, most of the botanical specimens in the backyard will not be available. However, it is a pretty safe bet that the ice-box will be able to make several very interesting contributions to our store. There are the tender, translucent celery leaves, apple skins, pieces of orange or lemon skin thinly sliced (with a razor blade), onion skin, a smear of yeast, or a bit of potato also sliced thin enough to pass a reasonable amount of light. Mother might also have a few plants that will yield not only botanical but biological specimens as well. Certain species of plant lice are rather common, and it is great fun hunting them. Rex, the dog, might also contribute a flea or two, and a stray, half-frozen spider left in the cellar might be forced to give his all in the interest of science.

If the search goes on patiently and we are not too superficial in our examination of specimens, we shall easily find enough material around the house to last us until spring. Of course, if we are going to peek at each new specimen for only a moment or two and then toss it aside on our refuse heap, we shall soon empty any house of images that are easily available and that do not require the kind of preparation that is beyond our skill. Such a neurotic expenditure of treasure will eventually deplete our reserve. The real fun comes in learning something about some of the subjects used. For instance, the examination of leaves, even those coming from celery and mother's plants, calls for the reading of an elementary book on botany, where we will learn something about cell formation, plant nourishment, cellulose, etc. Conducted in this enlightening manner, our hobby becomes a great generator of knowledge, and the world in which we live becomes an endless storehouse of staggering wonders ever challenging our imagination and skill.

Indeed, if we wished, we could spend the rest of our lives inspecting the microscopic wonders of the plants in the garden. We take the matter of starches. The vegetable kingdom yields a number of them, and once we learn to recognize them, we can set about comparing the starch grains from a potato with the starch grains of a kernel of wheat. Aided by additional information from the right book at the local library, an inquiring mind could easily be entertained for a whole month with this topic alone. On the other hand, if we are going to spend our coin of the realm of the microscope carelessly, we shall soon find ourselves bored in work that offers a lifetime of fascination.

Returning to the subject of leaves, again we find many opportunities to carry our investigation on for weeks and even months. And yet, this is but one of the hundreds of thousands of botanical and biological specimens that are available. The world abounds with them. They are under our very feet.

The mechanism of the cells found in leaves is wondrous indeed and at present little understood. The big guns of research have been trained on this investigation for some years in an attempt to reveal nature's process for the manufacture of sugar directly from water and carbon dioxide, the energy being

taken in some mysterious manner from the sun. In-
closed in each leaf is a strange chemical, green in
color (we might call it the green blood of plants),
named *chlorophyll*. In a manner as yet not discovered, this interesting chemical acts as some sort of
catalytic agent in the formation of the plant food,
sugar. It is a sort of go-between for the energy of the
sun and the carbon dioxide and water, effecting the

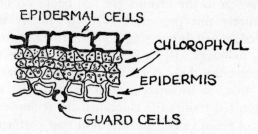

FIG. 10. Cross-section of leaf showing the arrangement of the
various cells. These cells may easily be seen by the microscopist.

union of energy with matter and the rearrangement
of the atoms involved without being changed itself.
Privileged indeed are we to peek in even momentarily upon one of the major mysteries of the world.
The Charles Kettering Foundation, of Antioch Col-
lege, Yellow Springs, Ohio, has concerned itself with
this mystery for a number of years. The solution
would have great industrial significance and would
lead to many important things of great use to human-
kind.

Leaves have a skin (epidermis) much like that of
animals, and, curiously enough, the skin of many

leaves may be peeled away. Such a simple procedure may be started with a razor blade, and it should be recalled that a piece suitable for our purpose does not need to be much larger than a pinhead. We are now in a world where things ordinarily considered small often turn out to be gigantic. We shall have to gain a new perspective. The words "large" and "small" will be more relative than ever.

If we go to the elementary text-books on botany, and surely this procedure is to be highly recommended, much interesting and pertinent matter relating to leaves will be discovered. It will be found that there are three essential parts to every leaf: the veins that, as in animals, run through the highly skeletonized frame; the chlorenchyma (composed entirely of green cells), and the skin that performs the same function as it performs in the animal kingdom. It holds the mass together giving it shape and form. It also in a measure prevents damage to the intricate interior of the leaf, especially damage by dust and other forms of contamination.

It will be fun to look at the drawings in the text-books and then to seek out their counterparts in the leaves we shall be examining. The nice part about a great deal of this microscopy of the common leaf is that it can be conducted without elaborate preparation and that the specimens are easily obtained.

The veins of a live leaf, we shall learn from our text-book, are quite busy. They have a three-fold function. They carry water received from the ground, distribute it, and carry protein and sugar back. Thus

the leaf gives and takes, and if we patiently search
with our instrument we shall finally turn from the
leaf with a sound knowledge of how it gets on in the
world. Of course, we could keep on studying the
structure of leaves for the remainder of our lives and
we should still leave behind us many things to be
learned.

As we look into leaves, we find that the stuff
dubbed chlorenchyma is made up of cells that may
rather easily be distinguished from the disk-like
grains of that marvelous chemical, chlorophyll. The
latter are bright green in color, and they also lack the
protoplasm found in the chlorenchyma cell. This
protoplasm is the life-bearing part of the plant or
leaf, and we find it literally swimming about in a
solution of sugar in water. It is also pressure-bound
in many plants, as a quick slit with a razor blade will
soon demonstrate. The leaf, if it is a fresh one, can
be seen actually to "bleed" through the rupture in
its skin.

While the life mechanism of all leaves is pretty
much the same, structure varies within comparatively
wide limits, and we shall be wanting to make a pretty
thorough study of all the leaves in the garden. There
is a considerable variation in the skin of leaves. One
would not surmise it, but the leaf of the hollyhock
looks rather ugly under the 'scope. The surface is
found to be covered with hairs or spines. In other instances, we discover scale-like formations, and in all
cases we shall find the well-known stomata, small
mouth-like openings distributed uniformly over the

surface of leaves. These are intimately connected with the life mechanism.

While speaking of common specimens around the house or garden, we should not forget hairs, both human and animal. Off-hand, it might be thought that a hair was a hair and that any activity here might prove to be pretty boring and monotonous. Not so. Considerable variation is found in hairs. A sheep's hair may be pulled from a sweater. Compared with a human hair, this is coarse and uncommonly rough. Yet when we stop to think of it, the roughness of the sheep's hair or wool is very necessary in all felting operations like the manufacture of felt hats.

Curiously enough, and much to the surprise of the novice, most hairs, if examined closely enough, will be found to bear scales; overlapping scales, indeed, in the manner of fish scales. Magnification will have to be increased considerably to see them, but if we carry it far enough, they will be there. The hairs of a number of animals will be available to us: dogs, cats, mice, rabbits, sheep, cows, etc. My lady's furs will also yield some material not common to the native soil.

Although we are not as yet ready to consider the subject of specimen preparation, we can point out that all animal hairs are very greasy and that soaking them in a powerful solvent like carbon tetrachloride or alcohol for a few moments will be helpful in making them more pliant and clear.

Inasmuch as hairs are pretty small, we shall have to be using a magnification in the neighborhood of 350 or 400 diameters. As we move the focusing knob at this power and with this sort of specimen, which, microscopically speaking, is not especially flat, we shall be struck with the various views that will be seen. It will appear that several scenes present themselves, one melting into another as the knob is turned. Focus is critical at this magnification, and what we are seeing is the various levels of the hair through its cross-section. Each appears different, and indeed each one is different. The first stop will be on the top of the hair, where the scales will be plainly visible.

The beginner does not have to confine himself to botany, lush and fabulous as the field is. He may turn to animated things: to the sub-optical monsters that roam the surface of the earth in multitudinous forms. They get in our vinegar and our hair and even invade our bodies. Of course, the more dangerous of the breed should be left alone, but they are the smaller fellows anyway. There is plenty to be done with the larger members of the group. These we may find in the fishbowl, in the bottom of the near-by stagnant pond, in decaying fruit, and in many other places. The search for such specimens can turn into a very exciting venture. It may even carry us far afield: along the shores of lakes and oceans, in the woods or atop the mountains. In any event, it will be exciting and fascinating, and few indeed are the amateurs who do not warm up to the lure of this business once they slip over into the extensive animal kingdom, to the little beasties that wiggle and kick, dive and squirm.

Marine life of this kind is quite plentiful. This may not have occurred to us for the simple reason that such creatures have always been beyond our sight and also, perhaps, because we have never really given the matter a great deal of thought.

If we live near a pond or creek sluggish enough to encourage the growth of the water-lily, we can be assured of bringing a fine mess of life from the bottom. Such places are always comparatively shallow, and, what is encouraging, they always yield an abundance of teeming life.

Collection of such material is delightfully easy. The collector simply ties a bottle or phial to a stick or pole long enough to reach to the bottom of the pond or creek. A length of five feet is usually sufficient. The collector may wish to take several containers along and fill each one, using a different location each time one is filled. When the bottom of the water is reached, the hunter should press down hard to make sure that some of the submarine muck and mud is forced into the mouth of the container. Much of what we seek will be wallowing around in this uninviting stuff.

If we resort to the high-brow books on the subject, we shall be informed that a number of the little beasties we seek are grouped under the general heading of *Protozoa*. In general we might describe Protozoa as the simplest forms of animal life. They are invariably made up of but a single cell. We take the common and marvelous amoeba as an example. Quite wrongly, it is referred to as a simple form of life; our greatest scientists have sought its secret for many years—from the very moment they first saw it. Yet little or nothing is known about its mechanism. We may even be fortunate enough to see one divide or in the process of division. However, that will reveal very little.

The slimy layer of mud on the bottom of stagnant pools, ponds, and creeks is where the life we have been talking about abounds. The collector should also bring a gallon or two of the plain water back with him. This he can use to replenish the water in his jars containing the specimens. It will evaporate gradually, and this is the safest water to employ for renewing it. That coming from the household water system might have too much chlorine in it for the good of our little prisoners. Indeed, the chlorine was put in for just such little people as they.

Having made a nice bag of game, we shall be wanting to get back home with it for a look. A medicine dropper is used to transfer just a single drop of the water to a clean microscope slide. Using the highest power we have (250 diameters will be high enough), we start the hunt. Before long, we see something sweep past that might resemble a piece of cellophane in a hurricane. It will be one of the beasties, sure enough. Once we draw a bead on him, however, we can take a good look before he moves out of range. There will be times when he will rest, too.

In the accompanying drawing, Fig. 11, we show a number of the little fellows that may be discovered in a pond or creek with the simple equipment just

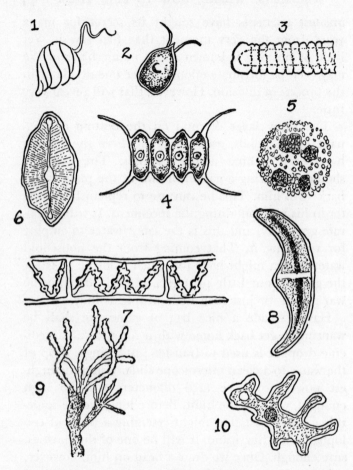

FIG. 11. Some of the plants and animals that may be seen by the novice. The objects numbered from 1 to 8 are algae found in almost stagnant water. At 9 we see a hydra, and an amoeba is illustrated at 10. These were all drawn from life; such work tends to make the microscopist's note-book alive and interesting.

mentioned. These drawings will help us recognize them once we come upon them. Pity the poor microscopist who does not make some effort to identify the strange creatures that sweep past his vision! Therein lies a great deal of the fun and most certainly therein lies a great deal of the education we shall be taking from our hobby. This sort of life is so abundant, however, that we can not hope to catalogue even a fraction of it here. The serious student or hobbyist is advised to buy, or borrow from his library, a textbook dealing with such life. These books provide positive identification for practically all the little fellows we shall be seeing. Actual drawings and photographs are supplied. From such books we learn, too, that our biologists have divided the Protozoa family up into Infusoria, Mastigophora, and Sarcodina.

The Sarcodina are the simplest of the lot, and all members of the family have a common characteristic in that they move about by extending or reaching out with a part of the protoplasm making up their frail bodies. The projections are used as feet until they are drawn back into the body of the creature. In this respect the action of the amoeba is of particular interest. Indeed, if we have a sense of humor, the first sight of an amoeba "going places" will tickle our funny-bone. In going about, the amoeba projects a bit of itself and then the rest of its body flows into the projected portion. This is done over and over again as the little creature moves along.

Another thing: we can be led to believe that the amoeba has rudimentary emotions. At least, it appears that it has some semblance of fear, for when we first drop it upon a slide and view it, we note that it no longer seeks to gad about but remains motionless in the form of a tiny ball. After waiting for some time, it moves rather timidly at first, and finally becomes daring enough to lapse into its rather odd stride.

Just as an example of what might happen if we "stick around" long enough, the feeding of the amoeba might be mentioned. It is a hungry little beastie and, glutton-like, simply wraps itself around its food and goes to work. This is an interesting thing to watch, and well worth waiting for.

All sorts of odd-shaped creatures will float across our vision in the examination of the pond water. Some of the forms will be utterly fantastic and grotesque. There will be Arcella vulgaris, living in a doughnut-like shell, Flagellates that move about with things that look like cats-o'-nine-tails, Valvox glabator that roll on end, etc. It is lots of fun, watching and studying these funny creatures, and we shall be doing a lot of it. Perhaps weeks of peeping will be required before we are introduced to a few of the members. Seeing them all would be asking too much for a beginner. Even some of the old-timers have not come face to face with the rarer specimens. Rare or not, they are all interesting and worth watching.

The field of the amateur microscopist is as large, really, as the world is large. One marvels constantly at the seemingly unending pattern of life and design that is found in the microscopic part of creation.

The most prosaic and unimaginative among us must confess that it is breath-taking. And the color! Unlike the camera, our microscope does not lie to us. It turns out to be pretty sincere, barring certain limiting technical imperfections, and color stands for what it really is. The most delicate hues are transmitted. The hues and shapes, indeed, put birds, flowers, and sunsets to shame. The limits of the grand sweep of color will never be ours until we spend a spell at the business end of a small microscope.

Coming back to the matter of specimens, we can find other things in the ice-box besides celery leaves and orange peelings. If our microscope will reach down into the optical well of life for a distance of 500 diameters, we can bring into view some of the more common bacteria that live in milk. Buttermilk, too, is rich in "bugs," and one does not have to look far in this medium for a flock of ugly denizens of the microscopic sub-world.

Yeast is fun, too, and a small cake of it can be made to yield educational entertainment that might last for a week or more. We discover, perhaps much to our amazement, that the homely yeast cake is quite a little bundle of marvels.

Setting the stage for the yeast drama is simple enough. Yeast contains certain things which, if given half a chance, will go to work with tremendous energy. Things called yeast plants grow in syrupy gardens, and the hobbyist can have a lot of fun watching them.

Yeast tablets or a small piece of ordinary grocery-store yeast cake can be used in our work. In either case, the yeast is simply dropped into a glass containing water that has been mixed (fifty-fifty) with syrup: corn syrup, that is. The syrup forms a rich "soil" in which the plants of our strange garden will grow rapidly.

This mixture is set away in a warm place for a day or two. Upon returning to it, we take a sample from the most murky part of it with a medicine dropper. A bit of this, not more than a drop, is placed on a clean slide, and we take a peek at the smear, using about 250 diameters. Soon we shall notice some little round objects, most of them with a sort of growth, also round, attached.

By observing the yeast plants over a comparatively short time, the generation of plant life on a grand and interesting scale can be seen. The round protrusions carried by many of the plants are nothing more or less than baby plants, and we can watch them mature and finally grow their own young. This is a curious sight, little chains being formed and finally breaking up to have each member in turn start another one of its own. It will be with some reluctance that we shall leave our micro-garden of wonders to investigate the many other green fields that lie directly ahead.

The algae department of amateur microscopy is filled with a form of splendor that is really astounding. We shall view it with open mouths. Here abide forms of beauty, design, and color so utterly fascinating that many newly arrived hobbyists have been

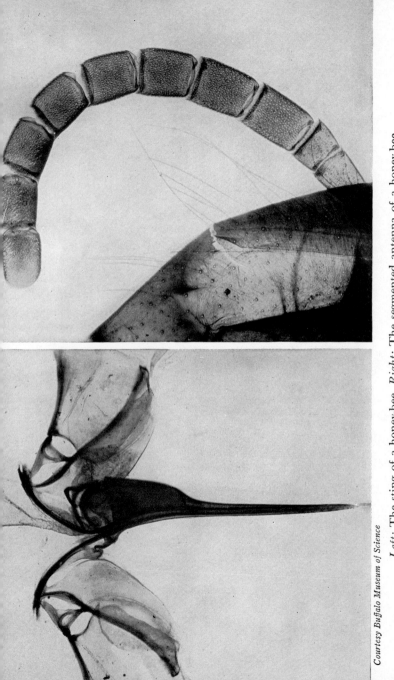

Courtesy Buffalo Museum of Science

Left: The sting of a honey-bee. *Right:* The segmented antenna of a honey-bee.

Courtesy Buffalo Museum of Science

Left: The crystals of cane sugar. *Right:* The yeast cell.

The ocular and objective removed. The ocular is sometimes called the eyepiece.

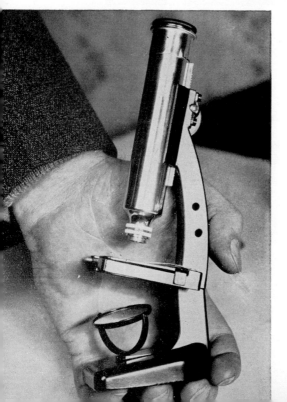

This little instrument cost $18.50, and should last a lifetime. Auxiliary lens equipment may be purchased.

The water-drop microscope complete and
ready for use.

The mirror is mounted on a block of white pine, and the
standard is formed with heavy iron wire.

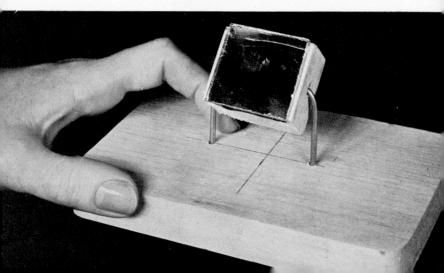

A home-made dissecting microscope the body of which is cut from 2 x 4 lumber.

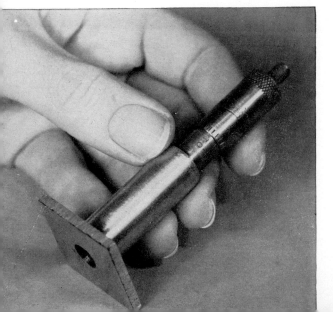

A fine microtome made with a 25¢ micrometer found in the chain stores.

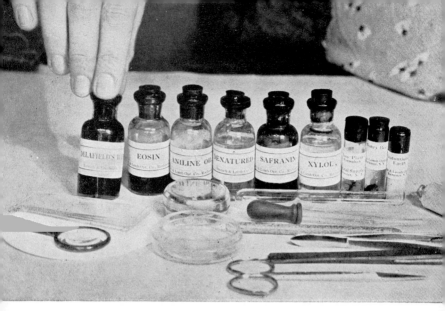

A complete set of stains for the amateur microscopist.

Covering a biological specimen with a stain.

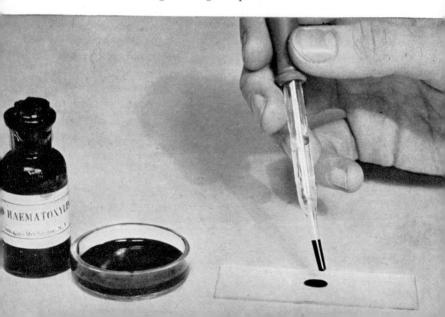

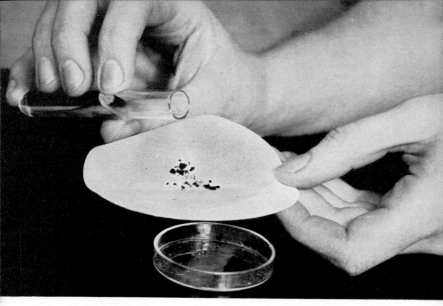

Washing a specimen with alcohol, using filter paper. Some biological specimens should not be permitted to soak in it.

Slipping a cover-glass in place after it has been covered with balsam. It is best to handle them with tweezers.

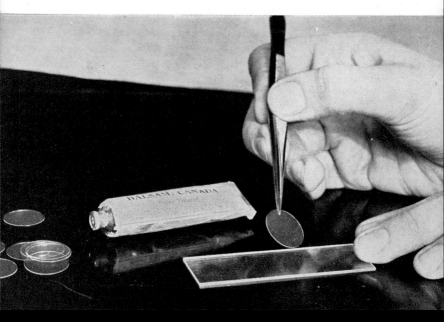

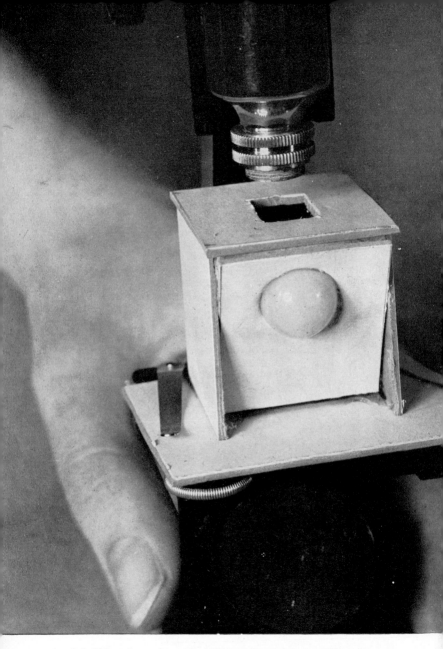

A half-hour's work making this smoke chamber with cardboard and a marble will be repaid with many hours of fascinating observation.

Courtesy Bausch & Lomb

A manufactured micro-projector for use with an amateur microscope.

The principal materials of this home-made micro-projector are a piece of 8 x 10 ground glass, serving as a screen, and some heavy cardboard.

With this simple, home-made device two people may use the microscope simultaneously.

This binocular attachment was made at home for three dollars.

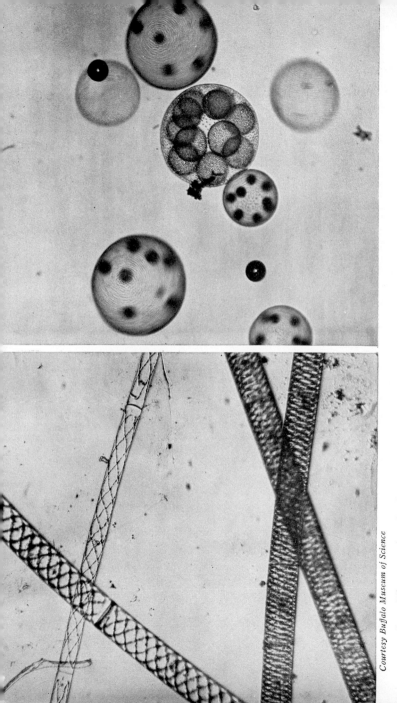

Courtesy Buffalo Museum of Science

Left: Three species of spirogyra found in stagnant water. *Right:* Volvox perglobator, which the hobbyist may find in the ponds, creeks, and ditches in open fields.

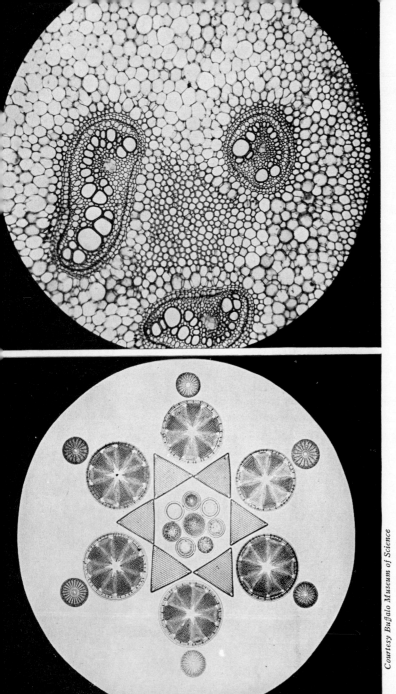

Left: A number of types of diatoms arranged in a design. *Right:* A cross-section of the rachis of brake fern.

known to linger for a year or more before leaving this microscopic fairyland.

A number of different forms of algae are found in ordinary stagnant water, and the mess we brought home previously will be no exception. The algae are dynamic, too. They move about, demonstrating various and often weird forms of locomotion. And strangely enough, at least from a purely physical viewpoint, none appears to be related. They assume all sorts of shapes. Some are round, some are rod-like, some are like small pears and others like two-headed beetles. Color? Well, all that can be said here is that the color is simply terrific!

As a single department in the study of algae, we take the specimens in the Desmid family. Here is a tribe crowned with exquisite beauty, every member of it. Then there is the family called Spirogyra, beautiful beyond words and commonly available throughout the world. One facet of the many-sided algae study is the study of diatoms. Here we enter a theater of activity so great that there is no hope of our living long enough to cover it completely. A special science has grown up around it, called diatomology.

We shall find our diatoms in the muck from the bottom of creeks and ponds, and they will amaze us. It will be a little difficult to realize that such shocking beauty can lie buried in such a revolting mess. But there we find them in endless forms. If, upon pawing over this stuff, as it were, we come upon something that stands out like a jewel because of its sheer beauty, the chances are that we have struck a mem-

ber of the family of diatoms. They are plentiful beyond words, and we shall not need to search for
them. They will pop up whether we like it or not.
When they do, we shall find ourselves quite taken up.

Diatoms have comparatively short lives, but they
remain dead for millions of years without losing any
of their form. Here and there on the surface of the
world, there is a large deposit of what is called diatomaceous earth. This is made up largely of diatoms
millions of years old. They are practically pure silica
(just like sand), and this accounts for their remark-
able state of physical preservation. Dug from their
prehistoric burial grounds, they come packed together, and in this form they have considerable commercial importance. Being mildly abrasive, they are
used in metal polishes and also in toothpaste. Little
did we realize when we brushed our teeth this morn-
ing that the bodies of plants that died millions of
years ago helped us with the job. Most toothpastes
hold a liberal amount of such material. Indeed, if it
is winter and we yearn to get at the bottom of that
near-by creek come spring, perhaps we can assuage
the desire by tapping the toothpaste for dead rather
than nice, fresh, live diatoms.

A quick examination will soon tell us whether or
not our brand of toothpaste contains diatoms. We
mix or dilute a bit with water, permit it to settle,
pour off the clear solution, and smear a bit of the
residue on a slide. As we shift the slide under the
objective we should soon come upon a number of

different diatoms if diatomaceous earth has been used.

However, we do not need to deal with the carcasses of diatoms in summer. Live ones, countless billions of them, are ready at hand. Again the source is the stagnant pool. And live diatoms swim about in various ways. As we see them swirling around in a drop of water we will not know whether they are fish or fowl at first. Finally, however, we shall recognize them for what they are, neither fish nor fowl, but plants.

The Desmids are likely to make classification difficult, for here we have little things that are really quite close to the diatom family and not one whit less interesting, although not so profuse. They have no silica in their make-up, and they are also composed of two symmetrical parts, joined. Perhaps Siamese twins is the best term to apply to them when it comes to supplying data for recognition.

Really, when it comes right down to it, a beginner will want to be looking at the surface and on the inside of hundreds of things. Of course, a more or less aimless search of this kind with no other guide than curiosity is apt to develop boredom. Some things are pretty prosaic under the microscope. This will be true for practically all artificial products: man-made things like paper, cloth, synthetic or imitation leather, etc. Because of this, it is best for the beginner to lean on the experience of those who have gone on before him and who have searched out the things of beauty and interest that lie within the range of the type of instrument that the beginner will be using.

In searching the literature devoted to amateur microscopy, one eventually comes to the "hay infusion." This is a curious name for the thing, but perhaps the meaning will be clear to us as we press on with the experiment, which is made only in the interests of more specimens within the optical reach of the untutored amateur.

Preparation for the experiment is delightfully simple. We merely place a handful of chopped hay or dried grass in a quart of water and permit it to stand in a warm place for a few days. One does not have to wait for warm weather for this experiment. Wintertime preparation is just as easy if the infusion is placed where a temperature of seventy degrees or better prevails. Under these conditions all the dormant life in the hay will undergo regeneration, and before long we shall have a pool teeming with all sorts of strange microscopic creatures.

After the hay water, as we might call it, becomes good and "ripe," we take a bit from it by the aid of a medicine dropper, place a drop of it on a glass slide, adjust our microscope for about 100 diameters, and start off on another hunt. It will not be long before all sorts of strange creatures will be showing up. Some will look like those we saw in the stagnant pond water. Others will be quite new to us. All in all, we can plan on spending a number of evenings at home for the investigation of the new well of life that we have created by the magic of warmth and a touch of water. And that is something to ponder, "the magic of warmth and water"! Somehow or other, the mechanism of creation is lubricated with water, for without it life remains dormant or impossible. Some forms of life lie waiting to spring into action at the touch of a drop of the fluid. Without it, there is only potential life. Heat appears to be the form of energy required for the engines of creation, and it is the water that lubricates them.

When the gentle touch of spring stirs the countryside, many interesting forms of insect life come forth to greet the dawn of summer. After a winter confined to examination of more inanimate things, the hobbyist will welcome the opportunity of once more seeking his specimens in nature's great out-of-doors where many curious things abound. We shall want to be taking a look at the mandibles of beetles, at the tongues of honey-bees, the stingers of wasps, and the wings of dragon-flies. There is a wealth of investigation in wings alone, both transparent and translucent. Many surprises await us here. Who would think, offhand, that the wing of a butterfly might be covered with millions of soft downy scales laid like shingles? Everywhere we turn with the microscope, we find a new twist or a new turn to life.

When specimens are chosen from the larger insects, there will be no need for high-powered magnification during preliminary examination. It must be recalled that many of these things will be millions of times larger than the little bugs at which we have been looking. Hence the need of using less magnification. Once we pick out some particularly small organ of an insect which we wish to examine more closely, we may turn to higher power. Here, however, we shall run smack into another problem, and that is the very special preparation required for such specimens. Some data for this will be presented subsequently in the chapter dealing with such matters.

An amateur living near the seashore will have an additional store of wonders from which to draw. The sea abounds in the kind of life that makes microscopy so interesting and so all-fired fascinating. Besides, after a few weeks of investigation with freshwater life, it will be added fun to see what sort of material nature has developed over the millions of years in salt water. We shall eventually discover that salt must have had a great deal to do with the sea life because things are so different here. The tempo of life is great and the variety is appalling.

Perhaps the most available common material that can be interesting is seaweed. The seaweed is interesting on two scores: by itself and with its guests. Such submarine vegetation becomes the abode of many forms of microscopic marine life, and if we bring our weed home with a bit of sea water to keep it in, the life will in a large measure be preserved.

Sea water, especially where it has stood in pools in the hot sun, is very apt to produce a horde of small life. The black muck lying in the flats near the seashore is always worth a week's fun if we sort a bit of it over. That does not mean merely a superficial glance at high power. It means a cautious sorting at low power—say 100 diameters.

Fish scales from either sea or fresh-water species are fascinating. The color coming from them, with proper illumination, is really fantastic. The iridescence is perhaps as good as we shall find anywhere, although it will vary a great deal.

When the flowers begin to arrive in the garden, the microscopist, now perhaps turned botanist, can conduct a most interesting investigation into pollen. And let it be known here and now that the subject of pollen is a big one. If we wish to read as we look, many interesting facts about pollination of flowers can be brought to light. It would be helpful if, during our investigation of pollen, we sought help from a book devoted to botany. There is a big story here and one which will hold our interest for a long time.

Many other commonly available objects may be had by the amateur microscopist, but the time will come sooner or later when he will wish to graduate from the kindergarten of the hobby and advance to more professional activities. To do this, he will need some instruction in the preparation of specimens that are not available for ordinary examination in their original state. The highlights of such preparation will be given in our next chapter.

5

Preparation of Specimens

WERE it not for special tricks that have been developed over the years, there would be many things that would not lend themselves to our work. Fortunately, by the use of such things as stains, razor blades, and other simple gadgets, plus a little more or less rapidly acquired skill, we shall be able to carry our research far beyond the present veil.

Before going further, perhaps a word or two of explanation might be necessary. Let us say that we wish to examine a comparatively large stem of a flower or weed, one about an eighth of an inch in diameter. We already know quite well that we can not force enough light through such a thing to take a good look. We know secondly that, even though we could, the specimen would be too thick to permit a general view. We could hope to be in focus with only one very limited level at a time. As we moved the objective lens up and down, we would see successive levels sweep by, but this would present a pretty confusing picture, and we would fail to get a very clear impression of the inside of our object.

Now let us assume that we have an extremely sharp knife and that we use it to cut a slice, in the manner of cutting bread, from the stem or stalk. Obviously, our knife should be sharp enough so that it will not crush the delicate fibers and ducts present in the object. The thinner the slice that can be cut, the better. More light will pass, and a truer picture of the structure at a particular level will be had.

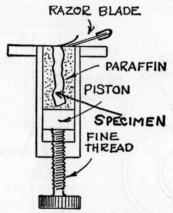

FIG. 12. The principle of the microtome.

Cutting such a slice is not quite as easy as it might sound to a beginner. After all, we are not manipulating a bologna sausage, and we are confronted not only with the problem of thinness but with the problem of crushing as well. How are we going to hold the specimen and how are we going to prevent some crushing, no matter how sharp the razor blade?

Many years ago, the microscopist devised an ingenious answer to this rather difficult question. An instrument called a microtome was devised. Our drawing, Fig. 12, will reveal the principle of this device. It will be seen that the specimen to be cut or sliced is held in place by the simple expedient of imbedding it in paraffin. The specimen is arranged within a small metal tube in such a manner that by simply turning a small screw, it can be made to pro-

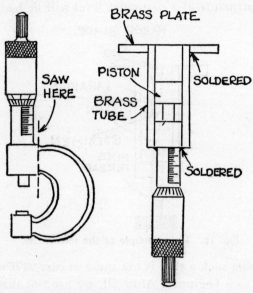

Fig. 13. A fine home-made microtome that will equal the performance of a five-dollar instrument may be made with a 'fifty-cent micrometer such as is found in the chain stores.

trude from the tube to a measurable degree. It is at this point that the razor blade comes forward to slice off the protruding section, which should not be any thicker than the crudeness of the method dictates. Of course, some objects prepared in this manner will be less transparent than others, and here we must aim at a thickness not to exceed 1/1,000 of an inch. This is by no means unattainable if we employ a sharp razor blade. The small economy of using a discarded blade is not advised. Indeed, the blade we employ for this purpose can not be too sharp.

Microtomes may be had for prices ranging from five to one hundred dollars, but we can make a very serviceable one for twenty-five cents. Here we refer to Fig. 13. Naturally, in the construction of an instrument of this kind, accuracy and fineness of adjustment are prime factors. Thus good use can be made of a small twenty-five cent micrometer such as we find on the counters of the five-and-ten-cent stores. These are intended for machinists. They are calibrated in such a way that we may actually measure within a very close range the thickness of each cut or slice made.

These little micrometers are applied to our purpose in the simple manner shown in Fig. 13. Before setting about with the actual construction of the device, it might be advisable to study this drawing carefully. Both the materials and the tools needed may be found about the household.

Some specimens that we shall be carving up will be sensitive to heat, and for that reason we should make a practice of heating the wax or paraffin only to a point where it will flow. This does not need to be as high as boiling water, and at such temperatures there will be little risk of destroying our specimen, whatever it may be. On the other hand, paraffin can be carried to a very high temperature where it becomes dangerous to handle because of the possibility of fire. At such temperatures, it is destructive to most specimens. Perhaps the safest way to melt it is to place the container in a pan of water and then heat the water.

After we have assembled the microtome, we had best try it out immediately. In each case we try to cut our specimens as thin as possible. These should be just able to hold together, and, of course, we shall have to use caution in transferring them to a microscope slide. It is also to be pointed out here that insect and animal tissue is usually much more perishable and crushable than is vegetable, and more care and caution will have to be used in its preparation.

For the preparation of animal specimens, we shall have to have not only the aid of a microtome but the aid of a dissection microscope as well. As the drawings in Fig. 14 will indicate, this, too, may be assembled in the home workshop at low cost. This device is really nothing more or less than a small table or hand rest equipped with a low-powered magnifying glass (not over 10x) and mirror, so that adequate light may be had while the microscopist is at work. Such accommodations may be established by arranging a small mirror at a 45° angle. The dissecting table itself is made of a piece of ordinary window-glass, although a piece of plate glass would be better if it could be had.

The drawing of the device is so complete and the device itself is so simple that no further description need be given here.

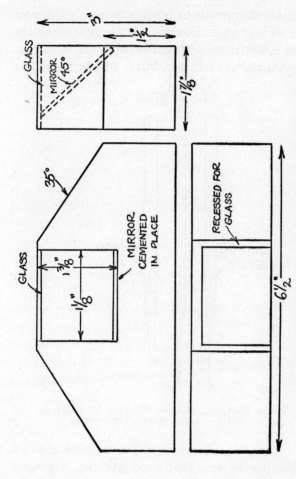

FIG. 14. The body of an excellent home-made dissecting microscope can be cut from a piece of 2 x 4.

If the microscopist is to butcher insects, frogs, and the like, he will have to have a complement of butchering tools. For those with adequate funds, it will be easy to purchase such things, but it will be more fun

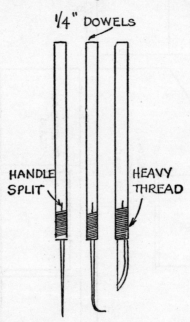

FIG. 15. These dissecting instruments may be made in the home workshop using dowels for handles.

to make them. The drawings in Fig. 15 show a series of simple instruments that need not cost a penny. The reader is also referred to the model airplane supply houses, where he may purchase holders intended for use with interchangeable blades of various shapes and types. It happens that some of these blades are just as desirable for use in cutting tissue as they are in slicing balsa wood, and here a twenty-five-cent investment is able to produce rich results. If the blades are honed on a fine stone, they become sharper still, and they will be most useful in chopping up insect parts.

We shall also be needing a small pair of scissors and one or two pairs of tweezers. The scissors should be of the type that are available at the drug-store for cutting hangnails and the like. Here we indulge ourselves to the extent of buying the best that we can afford. A cheap pair will usually turn out to be troublesome, and we shall be called upon to cut delicate things that are often difficult. If the cutting edges of the scissors do not come together properly, they will do anything but cut.

Tweezers, too, should be of a good grade. One can anticipate the trouble that might be had in trying to grab a thin membrane between the tips or jaws of tweezers that did not come together. However, by the use of very fine files and a fine stone, we may so treat the tips of even the cheapest tweezers that they will come together properly and maintain a grip upon the thinnest specimens.

We remain a long way from professional technic until we achieve the technic of using stains in microscopy. Although it is, of course, the better part of wisdom to keep our specimens clear and transparent, so that all light possible will get through them, we often come to specimens whose various parts are so uniformly transparent that it is difficult and at times even impossible to distinguish one part from another. In short, there is a serious lack of contrast. Such difficulties are overcome by the use of stains of various colors. These stains are absorbed by some tissues more than by others, and in this way we are able to emphasize contrast. It also happens that some tissue is more sensitive to one stain than to another, and in such cases two or more stains are applied to a single specimen in an effort to reveal structure. The subject of stains and staining is so important as the more professional aspects of microscopy are approached that one can not hope to carry his hobby to its apex of enjoyment unless the use of the simpler stains is mastered.

Fortunately, the stains we shall be using are inexpensive. Chief among them we find iodine of the ordinary drug-store variety. We can make up our own solutions, using one part tincture of iodine with five parts of alcohol. A drop of this on some specimens will render them far more visible, and perhaps, in some cases at least, the colors developed will surprise you. They are not all necessarily brown. Some will be high yellow, and others, as in the case of starch granules, for instance, will be deep blue, because of the well-known chemical reaction between those two materials.

Perhaps eosin is the most widely employed dye or stain used in microscopy. We shall want an ounce bottle of it, and in the examination of some animal tissues and a great deal of vegetable matter, it will be invaluable. The colors produced by eosin will normally be either red or pink, and the results are often magical. Eosin is really a dye, and it may be purchased in powder form. It is dissolved in alcohol for use. Only a small amount should be added to an ounce of alcohol. The resulting solution should be fairly transparent and not so deep as to cut off light. Thus we add the dye to the alcohol until the proper point is reached. If too much is used, then the solution may be diluted with more alcohol.

Most amateur microscopists aspire to view bacteria at some time or another during their careers. In that event, they will have to give some thought to the stain or dye called methylene, which comes for the use of the microscopist in a form called Loeffler's Solution. Not only is this preparation widely used in bacteriological work, but it is also useful in viewing a number of specimens more in line with early experiences. Hence, we should stock a small bottle of the stuff. Oftentimes our local druggist will have it made up, but in the event he does not, we can hand him the following prescription:

Saturated solution of methylene blue in 30 cc. of alcohol

100 cc. of water + two drops of 10% potassium hydroxide solution

As we move along in our work and consult the various authorities, we shall sooner or later come upon references to this important stain. Then we shall have it at our finger-tips ready for instant use.

What has become known as the Delafield formula for hæmatoxylin should also be among the modest collection of stains at hand. Few druggists will know how to put up this formula, and it is best that we send to a supply house for an ounce or two. It does not cost a great deal, and as time wears on we shall have plenty of opportunity to make good use of it. Every textbook relating to the subject of the preparation of specimens for examination makes wide mention of it.

Then there is carmine. Most experienced microscopists like to put up their own brand, and this is quite simple and certainly inexpensive. We take a bit of the red powder, say a bit on the end of a teaspoon, and place it in two or three ounces of water. The mixture is stirred before ammonia is added. Upon the addition of this ingredient, the carmine will pass into solution quickly. We do not stop here, however. The resulting solution is slowly heated until all the liquid has been evaporated. This will leave a red solid in the bottom of the dish. This is redissolved in plain distilled water, and the solution is then filtered through paper.

The textbooks will mention many other stains, many rather expensive and some of them quite difficult to prepare. Doubtless we shall find, as we move along, that most of the common specimens that come to our hands for examination may be adequately viewed with the few stains or dyes in our collection. Certainly we do not want to burden ourselves now with chemicals that we do not know how to use. Better to develop and polish our technic first with the materials mentioned.

We now proceed to make our first use of stain. Some of the common stains will permit a better look at most of the specimens we have been discussing. Others are best used in a rather narrow range, but in any event most specimens have but one dye with which they may best be seen. As time goes one, we shall become familiar with the best dye to use in each instance, and then, perhaps, we may wish to increase our stock and specialize a little more.

As a good example of the use of stain, we turn for a moment to bacteria of the type we will find in a smear of ordinary buttermilk. If our microscope will carry us up to 500 diameters, these bacteria will become easily discernible, but not without some preparation. Therefore, the smear is permitted to dry, after which a drop or two of grain alcohol is put in place and ignited. Such fixation of the beasties is followed by an application of methylene blue with a medicine dropper. After this, a drop or two of grain alcohol is applied and the whole thing rinsed gently in distilled water. If the job has been done neatly and skilfully, we should have an excellent specimen of our little bugs permanently fixed for our collection, if we wish to put a cover-glass in place according to directions that follow in another chapter.

The art of butchery as practised by the microscopist calls for skill and the fine touch. Perhaps the beginner will for some time limit his investigations to such things as insects, tadpoles, minnows, and the like. In that event, the instructions that follow will serve his interests. Of course, it is assumed that the young scientist now has the dissecting instruments previously mentioned as well as the simple dissecting microscope which is so easily constructed. Without these rudimentary pieces of equipment, biological investigation should be postponed.

The novice should not become too ambitious in his first adventures in the biological field. He is going to be "all thumbs" when he starts, and he might just as well become reconciled to the fact. From a microscopic viewpoint, most insects are monstrous creatures, and a careful examination calls for piecemeal dismemberment.

First, the insect is dispatched: murdered in cold blood by total asphyxiation in a bit of cotton saturated with ether or chloroform. This may be placed in a small phial; the insect, kicking and struggling, perhaps, is pushed in also and the cork inserted. Within a half-hour or so the insect will be in insect heaven, and we may proceed with the gruesome business of dismemberment.

The lifeless fellow is placed on the glass of the dissecting microscope, while we look him over with the low-powered lens. Making good use of our tweezers and scissors, we proceed to help ourselves to a wing, a leg, a proboscis or any other entomological tidbit that happens to strike our fancy. We must proceed with care, however: not out of respect for the poor fellow on the operating table, but because we do not want to damage our specimens any more than necessary. Most of them will be easily crushed or broken, and so destroyed they offer very little in the way of education. If some of the components are too large, then they in turn may be pulled apart.

We must not expect to graduate from the kindergarten of microscopy too soon. Before we push into the general anatomical inspection of insect interiors, we had best keep to exteriors until we acquire a reasonable amount of skill or at least learn to manipulate tiny parts without rendering them totally unsuitable for microscopic investigation.

Assuming that this has been done, we can move into the more difficult field of interior inspection. Here, however, and quite apart from any skill that we may have developed, we shall be able to do little more than satisfy our morbid curiosity unless we preface our work with some of the lighter reading in the field of insect life. There is little point in rummaging around inside a water beetle when we can not distinguish between his heart and his kidneys. Although our respect for insects has perhaps never been very high, we must remember that even the simplest present wondrous mechanism has been built up around the central mystery of life and that great skill is required to remove, preserve, and examine parts of insect bodies.

The victim, after being killed, is pinned, back down, on a piece of heavy cardboard. It is assumed here that the amateur will wish to make an abdominal approach to insect interiors. Perhaps we shall want to limit our first venture to the stomach alone, which would be sensible. Here it must be recalled that the stomachs of insects are usually located in the hindquarters, and the research begins there.

Before a vent is made with the smallest dissection knife, the body, cardboard and all, is placed in a shallow dish of water, and the incision is made under water. Carefully the skin is grasped with the forceps or tweezers and pulled back. If a good job has been done, the whole interior of the insect's body will have been laid open, and we may thereafter help ourselves to the various organs. At this point we shall be glad that we took on a little preliminary study. Otherwise, the whole business would be pointless and utterly unintelligible.

Operations on some of the hard-skinned fellows like beetles and cockroaches may be greatly facilitated by soaking them in water for several hours. Such soaking may be carried on in a watch glass. This will be found to be well suited for use with the dissection microscope.

The microscopist, amateur and professional alike, is always seeking ways of increasing the range and depth of his vision. And both amateurs and professionals have, over the years, devised many simple and ingenious ways of bringing this about. In some instances, special mechanisms have been employed for this purpose, and in later chapters we shall have plans for some of these things. For the moment, we are interested in a scheme that requires no mechanism of any kind. Reference is made to what has become known as collodion casts. The casts are made with ordinary collodion available at any drug-store, and they are used to further the study of surface formations. Collodion, due to its being a solution of guncotton in the powerful and extremely volatile solvents, ether and alcohol, is extremely fluid, and, once the solvents have evaporated, which they do quickly upon exposure to air, there is left a hard, flinty, transparent film. This can very easily be peeled off, and it will have formed on its underside an exact impression of the surface upon which it formed. The faithfulness of these impressions will astound us. They are complete in every detail.

It will be clear, however, that collodion impressions or casts can not be applied to all surfaces. A substance must be hard enough to resist removal of the film, and it must also remain unaffected by the powerful solvent action of the ether and alcohol. As objects that lend themselves to such surface examination, we might mention an oyster shell or the hard (chitin) wings of a beetle.

The very nature of light makes it extremely difficult to examine some things. Ordinary light reaches our specimens in every-which-way—from all possible angles. On the other hand, what is known as polarized light strikes an object always on the same plane; it travels with soldier-like formation. A better idea of what is meant may be had by referring to Fig. 16. If one end of a long rope is fastened and we yank the free end, a wave-form or ripple will run along the rope and finally reach the fixed end, where the disturbance, really a moving wave, will be destroyed.

Except for the size of the wave and the fact that it traveled over a very tangible medium, light waves act in much the same manner. However, some vibrate sidewise, some vertically, etc.

To polarize light, we permit ordinary light to pass through an optical arrangement that holds back all waves save those in a definite plane. We can un-

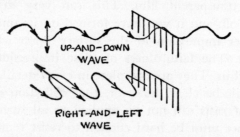

FIG. 16. Polaroid glass or celluloid has a selective action on light waves, permitting only those on a definite plane to pass. This would be much like causing ripples along a rope to pass through a comb-like arrangement. Only those moving up and down would succeed.

derstand the principle involved by making another examination of Fig. 16. The up-and-down waves along the rope or string can pass through the comb. The right-and-left waves can not. Optical arrangements have been devised whereby this selective action is very pronounced, and so-called polarized light is thus made available for microscopic work.

Fortunately, polarizing attachments may be purchased for a small junior microscope at low cost, or, as we shall see later, we may make such a gadget with little expenditure of either time or money. We shall be surprised, too, at the perfectly wondrous results that may be had with such illumination. Things that appear under ordinary illumination in one way will, under polarized light, have a totally different and wholly unexpected aspect. Colors will be magnificent and quite beyond words. Structure will often show up in some unexpected form, and our knowledge of things examined will be enriched to a very large extent. In metallurgy and mineralogy, the use of polarized light is absolutely essential.

Crystals, too, are often very difficult to examine with ordinary illumination, especially the white ones, as in the case of sugar. We look at some of the smaller grains of sugar (the smaller ones *pass* more light and are therefore more difficult) and find close examination quite impossible. However, if we have a polarizing attachment at hand we shall soon discover that marvelous effects and increased visibility may be attained in a jiffy.

Polarized light usually shows up best with crystals, and for that reason we shall extend our experiments beyond peering at a few grains of sugar. First we shall dissolve some epsom salts in water; say a teaspoonful in about ¼ glass of warm water. The warm or hot water serves two purposes. First, we want a saturated solution of the salt and, second, we do not want to wait too long for it. Salts dissolve more quickly in warm water.

We now take a clean glass slide and place a few drops of the solution on it. This is placed on a level spot (so the drops will remain in place) and the water of the solution is permitted to evaporate. After this has happened, we will find a crystalline deposit of the salt on the slide. It is this that we seek.

Before the crystals are examined with the polarized light, we take the precaution of placing several drops of medicinal mineral oil over the crystal deposit and

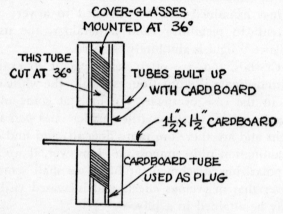

FIG. 17. How a home-made polarizing attachment may be had using only cardboard, paper, and a few cover-glasses.

then place another clean slide over the oil. The preparation is then ready to be slipped under the clips on the stage of the microscope and viewed with the aid of the polarizer. Through the use of the mineral oil and the second slide, bad reflections can be prevented and greater enjoyment may be had. No comment will be made on the strange beauty that becomes visible. Left to discover it for himself, the hobbyist will enjoy a greater thrill. What is more, words are weak when used to convey an impression of the exquisite nature of the spectacle.

Polarizing outfits intended for amateur use may be had for two dollars nowadays, but if the hobbyist

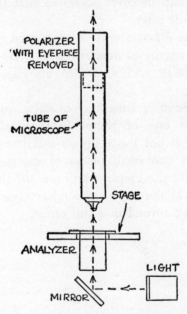

POLARIZER
'WITH EYEPIECE
REMOVED

TUBE OF
MICROSCOPE

STAGE

ANALYZER

LIGHT

MIRROR

FIG. 18. How the polarizing attachment is set in place on a microscope.

wishes, he may make one according to the directions in Fig. 17. The arrangement of the device within the microscope is shown in Fig. 18. Although we have not as yet mentioned the cover-glasses shown in the drawing, we shall become acquainted with them in the next chapter. They are the thin, clear little disks of glass used to cover specimens that will be permanently mounted for our collection. When stacked in the manner shown, they can serve to polarize light, and the polarizing effect may be controlled by mounting one group of cover-glasses so that they may be turned a full 360°.

While the glasses shown are mounted in cardboard tubes, the ingenious amateur with good shop facilities may, if he wishes, mount his glasses in metal tubing.

There are several methods of polarizing light, and this is but one of them. Professional polarizing equipment is not made up on this principle. It involves only two small pieces of specially prepared glass, one for the eyepiece and one for the objective. The piece at the top of the microscope tube is arranged to be turned in a full circle.

6

Mounting Specimens for Keeps

WE have come a long way since taking our first peep, but we are still pretty much in our swaddling clothes. Indeed, we can never hope to vie with professional circles, even in a very small way, until we master some of the details and technic of specimen mounting. The well-trained microscopist is very clever at preserving specimens under glass, and many and ingenious are his methods for so doing. These can not all be covered here, but we can supply the beginner with directions for permanently preserving most of his pet subjects. Naturally, many of our specimens, being small and delicate, will not long remain uncontaminated either by dust and dirt or by actual decay. Others dry up and literally shrivel away. Others fade. Some come apart—fall to pieces.

Our first mounting kit does not need to cost a great deal. A few slides will be needed, a few cover-glasses, some Canada balsam, and a few odds and ends. The slides are made of good glass and they measure 1 x 3 inches. They are made of thicker glass than the cover disks. The specimens, after being prepared in one of a number of ways, depending solely upon the nature of the article to be preserved, are placed between the glass slide and the cover-glass and then sealed in place so as to exclude air and moisture.

The No. 1 part of our instructions relates to cleanliness. The word must be accepted in its broadest meaning. Merely to look through a cover-glass or a slide is not quite enough. They can still be microscopically dirty—crawling with micro-organisms that will make short shrift of certain specimens once they are locked up with them between glass. Germicidal cleanliness is also needed. There is no place for the careless, sloppy worker. Most of the specimens mounted by him will soon spoil, and he will discover, sooner or later, that he has merely found an interesting way of wasting his time.

Mountings may be placed in two rather general classifications: those in ordinary air and those made in some medium like balsam or glycerin. These two liquids are used a great deal because of what is known as their refractive index. By this is meant the degree to which they bend light waves when they pass through. It will be obvious, even to those without training in the physics of light, that the refractive index of any medium used should be as close to glass as possible if a high degree of optical distortion is to be avoided.

As we move along in our work and read the various authorities, we will realize that mounting is accomplished more often with glycerin or balsam than it is with air. This is not difficult to understand when it is recalled that nearly all our botanical and biological specimens contain water. Total removal of the water is difficult and often renders the specimen unsuitable. Mounting such specimens invariably eventuates in foggy slides due to evaporation. This should not be accepted as a total warning not to use such mountings at all, but it may be accepted as an index of possible trouble that amateur skill can not avoid. Some specimens will remain mounted in air for an indefinite period without suffering any deterioration. Others will rapidly decline.

The first step in any kind of mounting has to do with the cleaning of the slides. This is no ordinary washing with soap and water. However, if a slide is exceptionally dirty and greasy it might be advisable to use this method. Ordinarily, the slide to be used for mounting is first washed in xylol, which is a powerful solvent and which finds a number of uses in microscopy. After this preliminary treatment, the slide is immersed in a fifty-fifty mixture of alcohol and water, and there it is permitted to remain until the final preparations for immediate mounting have been completed. Only careless microscopists prepare slides and then permit them to lie about for hours before they are used.

Having issued our warnings in connection with the air-mounted specimen, we shall proceed to supply directions for such work. Perhaps if we refer to Fig. 19, the meaning of air mounting will become clearer. What is known as a cell must be created first. The cell is nothing more or less than an air space created between the slide and the cover-glass. Its diameter is always the same, but its depth will vary with the thickness of the specimen to be mounted. In any event, no matter what form of mounting is employed, the worker will wish to guard against damaging the specimen. Thus, in the case of air mounting, the air space between the slide and the cover-glass must be great enough so that crushing of the specimen will not result when the latter is put in place. In mounting a fly wing, the clearance would

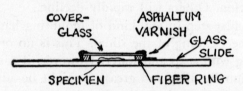

FIG. 19. Showing how a deep cell is formed through the aid of a washer.

not need to amount to more than a few thousandths of an inch. Other specimens might require a well or cell so deep as to make ordinary preparation too slow and tedious.

Properly to mount with the air method, what is known as a turn-table must be at hand if a professional job is to be done. Where thin specimens are mounted (and most specimens will be thin), the walls of the cell are built up by repeated applications of clear shellac or asphaltum varnish. Fig. 21 supplies all the details for the construction of a home-made turntable. After a little study, its use will be clear. First the slide is put in place and the tip of a small camel's-hair brush is dipped in either one of the materials mentioned. While turning the table with one hand, we bring the brush in contact with the slide near its center and describe a circle with an outside diameter slightly larger than the diameter of the cover. As we gain experience in this matter, we shall learn just how much pressure is to be exerted on the brush, and this in turn will determine the width of the deposited shellac or asphaltum varnish. The drawing, Fig. 20, will provide us with about the correct proportions.

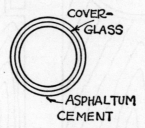

FIG. 20. How asphaltum cement is used to seal a cover-glass.

When comparatively thick specimens are to be mounted in this manner, a single application of shellac or varnish will not be sufficient. In such cases, we will leave our slide in place on the turn-table and put repeated applications of varnish or shellac in place, permitting each one to dry before a new one is added. Thus we slowly build up cell walls. It will be found that few specimens will require more than three or four applications.

Should greater cell depth be required, then we should turn to the use of fiber or cardboard washers. These are cemented in place on the glass slide with

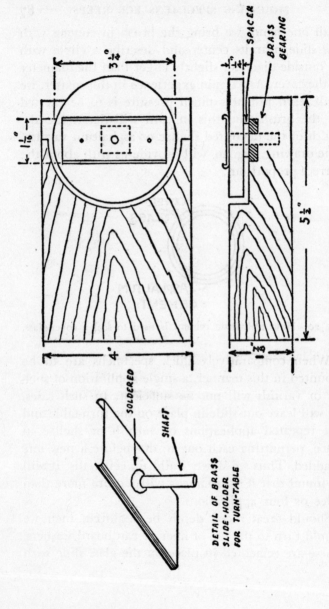

FIG. 21. Details of a simple home-made turn-table used in the preparation of slides.

Labels within figure:
3¾"
1¹⁄₁₆"
4"
⁷⁄₈"
SPACER
BRASS BEARING
5½"
³⁄₈"

SOLDERED
SHAFT
DETAIL OF BRASS SLIDE-HOLDER FOR TURN-TABLE

shellac or varnish, and they should be carefully covered all over to seal them. The cover-glass is set in place while a fresh application is made, and the edges of the cover-glass are carefully smeared with whatever mixture is used.

What is known as Mayer's albumin cement or fixative is used by professionals for holding cardboard or fiber rings to the surface of the glass. This cement will also be found useful for other things, and the amateur is advised either to purchase a small bottle of it or to make a batch. Making it is easy enough. Fifty cc. each of ordinary egg-white and glycerin are mixed together and then one grain of sodium salicylate is added. The result is shaken until thoroughly uniform and is then filtered. The cement becomes hard and strong after it has been applied and dried.

Glycerin mounts are easy to make, and they will last over long periods of time if ordinary care is exercised in their preparation. Of course, mounting of any kind is not for impatient or sloppy workers. To mount in glycerin, we shall need some glycerin jelly. This may be prepared on our bench from rather ordinary materials. One part of gelatin (from a package of mother's dessert, if need be) is added to six parts of distilled water, proportions being determined by weight. An equal amount of pure glycerin is then added, after which a few drops of carbolic acid are mixed in. After thorough mixing, the jelly is ready for use.

Actual mounting with this jelly is quite rapidly

done, but we are warned that specimens so mounted will not endure as long as mountings made by other means and with other materials. First, the glycerin jelly is gently warmed and the specimen to be mounted is put in place in the center of a clean glass slide. The melted jelly, which the heat in the meantime has made rather fluid, is poured over the specimen. A clean cover-glass is then immediately set in place on the surface of the jelly and gently pressed so as not to damage the specimen. Before long the jelly will set hard, and the specimen will be ready to add to our collection. Naturally, in handling this jelly we try to be as careful as possible to prevent smearing the stuff in places where it is not wanted.

Objects like plants need not have their water removed to be mounted in glycerin jelly. Thus the worker saves a great deal of time, if he wishes to sacrifice the longer lasting power of his preparations.

The less quick but, on the whole, more satisfactory method of mounting specimens with Canada balsam (a resinous gum from the balsam tree), may be divided into four stages. First, there is what is known as fixation; then come dehydration, staining, and clearing.

Fixation relates to the preservation of the cells of living matter, either animal or vegetable. As can well be imagined, these cells are extremely delicate, and they are easily destroyed. Hence great care in handling them must be exercised, and every effort must be made so to treat the cells as to preserve their original form. This is accomplished by what is known as a fixing solution, which acts to harden the cells so that they will hold their form as long as possible.

Two kinds of solutions are ordinarily employed by amateurs. One is a solution of corrosive sublimate (extremely poisonous when taken internally) and the other is merely a mixture of alcohol and water: one ounce of alcohol (grain) is added to two ounces of distilled water. Clean containers should be used for the solution to prevent specks being mounted along with our specimens.

The process of fixation is simple enough. Once the specimen has been cut loose from its surroundings, we place it in a few drops of the water-alcohol mixture and permit it to stand there for about fifteen minutes. It is then taken out and carefully rinsed in distilled water. Now it is ready for the next step which must be taken pronto. This is dehydration, and it is quite simple.

We carry it on with a series of alcohol solutions. Alcohol has a quick and ready appetite for water, and it will draw water from its surroundings when such an opportunity is extended. It follows that pure alcohol does this more quickly than a mixture. Long experience has shown, however, that the immediate introduction of our specimen to pure alcohol would be a little too violent. Thus we mix up four solutions of grain alcohol with water, ranging in strength from 50 to 95 per cent. The second is 75 per cent, the third 90 per cent. Thus the figures stand 50, 75, 90, 95. Should the worker take a short cut and skip all the weaker solutions, introducing his specimen to the 95 per cent solution first, the cells of the specimen would suffer considerably and they would also be distorted. The careful worker tries to avoid such damage. He is quite satisfied with the slower but much surer method.

The length of time for immersion in each solution depends upon the size of the specimen to be treated. Five to eight minutes is quite sufficient for small specimens, while larger ones will require fifteen to twenty minutes.

Enough has been said about staining to make the next step easy to accomplish.

The object must now be cleared: rendered as visible as possible. Here we seek to impregnate the cells of the specimen (assuming that it has cells) with a liquid that has the same index of refraction as glass. Obviously this calls for a liquid that will be miscible with both alcohol and balsam. Xylol or cedar oil may be employed. Rather than to load our little laboratory up with two things, however, it might be advisable to employ the xylol. This has many other uses also. Canada balsam, for instance, may be diluted with it, so that smears of the balsam may be removed from slides, etc.

The actual mounting of the specimen in balsam is easy enough after the routine outlined above has been followed through. We simply place a drop or two (depending upon the size of the specimens), upon a clean slide, set the specimen in it, and gently put a cover-glass in place.

Some workers use xylol with an equal amount of

balsam in making a balsam mounting. This makes the mixture very fluid, and the greater fluidity has its advantages.

Our catalogue of mounting methods that can be easily employed by the amateur will be completed by directions for the use of liquid petrolatum. The common drug-store variety may be employed. This material does not need to be heated, and it has rather fine optical properties. Unfortunately, the services that can be rendered by petrolatum in mounting are not complete. Specimens to be mounted in this medium should be dry. After the well or cell has been made, the liquid is set in place and the specimen is laid in it. We make sure that the specimen is totally covered, and then we put the cover-glass in position, but not until after we have run over the edge of the cell wall with a brush dipped in clear shellac. After this has dried, we cover the edge of the cell with asphaltum varnish.

While such work may sound somewhat dull to many of us, there is really not a dull moment in it. We shall find ourselves struggling to overcome our awkwardness, and the perfect result will ever be a challenge to us. Then, too, we shall be wanting to build up our collection. Each specimen mounted is given a name on a sticker mounted on the end of the slide, and we shall want to build little boxes with grooved sides for our growing library of marvels.

7

Photomicrography Is Easy

LAYMEN or amateur microscopists who have marveled at photomicrographs rarely realize that anybody, even without previous experience either with photography or with microscopy, may take such pictures. What is more exciting, perhaps, is the fact that excellent results may be had without a camera of any kind. Any home tinker can take an evening off and build an efficient substitute for a camera.

The novice will immediately ask where he is going to get his lens for such a camera. "Surely," he will be saying, "this will cost me more than a few pennies." The answer to this is that we do not need a lens of any kind. Indeed, when an ordinary camera is pressed into service for photomicrography, it is first necessary to remove the entire lens system. The need for this will become evident if we stop to examine Fig. 22. Here we discover that the lens of the microscope becomes the lens for the camera. We also find that the microscope is used as a small projector or magic lantern, the image being thrown on a screen which is a ground glass for focusing. After the focusing has been completed, the ground glass is replaced with a piece of film. The shutter of any camera may or may not be used. Exposure may be controlled with a switch which turns the illumination on and off. After a little experience is had in timing such ex-

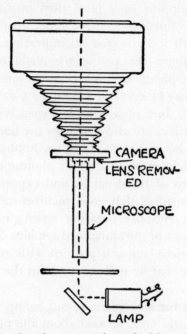

CAMERA

LENS REMOV-
ED

MICROSCOPE

LAMP

FIG. 22. How a focusing camera is used with a microscope for photomicrography. In this case, the lens of the camera is removed.

posures, any amateur may proceed to build up a photomicrograph library.

Before we push on to the details of equipment, something might be said about the size of the pictures. Exposures of any size may be made, even on 35 mm. film, but it will be clear that there is little need of making them any larger than is necessary. If one has a miniature camera and a projecting lantern, pictures may be taken with such equipment. It is also possible to employ such film when facilities are at hand to view finished pictures under good illumination and with low-powered magnification. For ordinary use, where the prints are made on regular photographic paper, sizes all the way from $2\frac{1}{4}$ x $2\frac{1}{4}$ up to 4 x 5 may be employed. The 4 x 5 size produces a nice print, but such film is expensive, and, of course, the prints are also costly. In the final analysis, size must be left to the choice of the hobbyist.

This much may be said about photomicrography: the conditions of illumination and exposure can be so nicely controlled that good pictures can not help being made, and the hobbyist setting out to bag some good shots of the embalmed remains of the little beasties of micro-land can proceed with ever-increasing assurance that he will return from the hunt with a nice haul.

Returning for a moment to our set-up illustrated in Fig. 22, little need be said about the photomicrographic principles involved. They are simple enough. The matter of focusing, however, should not be tossed aside too lightly. For good focusing we shall need a camera with a ground glass back. The specimen to be pictured is placed on the stage of the microscope in the standard manner, and the illumination is adjusted to provide an even field not too bright. An over-bright field is very apt to produce a lack of contrast in the negative; the beginner is also more likely to make an over-exposed negative.

In focusing for a picture, the camera is first dispensed with, and the object is brought to heel in the ordinary manner. Then the camera is moved into place without lens, and the photographer moves his point of vision from the eyepiece of the microscope to the ground glass back of the camera. Here he may wish to make adjustments not only in focus but also in the degree of illumination. An image that may be bright enough for good observation with the microscope alone may not show up well enough on the ground glass, because of the additional light needed for projection. Here it would be nice to have a rheostat control on the electric bulb used in the illuminating device. We may then merely "turn the lamp up," as it were.

Focus is sharp, and it follows that focus may also be readily destroyed. For this reason, a home-made camera for photomicrography is on the whole more convenient and fool-proof than an ordinary camera stripped for this particular use. After focusing with the ordinary camera, we must insert the plate or the cut film, and this may easily destroy or at least injure the focus which we had. With the home-made equipment, it is necessary only to lift the ground glass from its position and replace it with the uncovered film ready for exposure. Here it will be clear that we must work in a dark room and without a shutter. We must also see to it that the surface of the film to be exposed occupies the same plane as the ground glass so that the focus will be preserved as far as possible. This interchange can be made so carefully that no damage to the focus can possibly result. Naturally, *all* lights, including the one used in the microscope illuminator, must be turned out while we take the cover from our cut film or plate holder. The exposure is controlled entirely by the light in

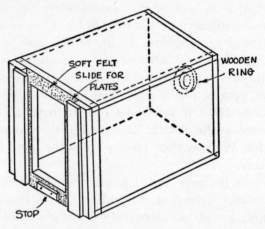

SOFT FELT
SLIDE FOR
PLATES

WOODEN RING

STOP

FIG. 23. Details of home-made camera for use with microscope.

the illuminator. After the exposure has been made, the cover is put back on the holder and arrangements are made for the next exposure.

Perhaps it would be wise to devote a little time to directions for the construction of the special camera. We try to make it as workmanlike as possible, seeing to it that the joints are all perfectly light-tight and that the interior of the box is painted a dull black (eggshell finish) to prevent unwanted reflections. Means will also have to be provided to make a light-tight joint between the eyepiece of the microscope and the opening in the front of the camera.

Perhaps the simplest guarantee against the intrusion of unwanted light between the camera and the eyepiece of the microscope can be had by making a tube of black cloth that can be placed between the

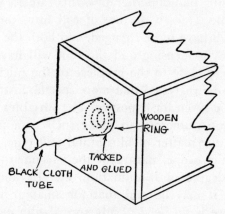

Fig. 24. How a black cloth tube is used to connect microscope with camera. A rubber band is placed around the microscope end.

two. Two thicknesses of the cloth can be used, and the seam of the tube should be double-sewed on a machine. A rubber band may be used to hold the one end of the tube over the eyepiece of the microscope.

The size of the camera may be adjusted to suit the needs of the work being done and especially the size of the film that is to be employed. In the case of a 4 x 5 film, the camera should be approximately nine to ten inches in length and about six inches square. The distance between the ground glass and the eyepiece of the microscope alone will determine the size of the image projected. As the microscope is moved away from the ground, the image will become larger. Thus we will understand that should we use 35 mm. film for our photomicrographs, this camera will not be suitable. Due to the use of roll film, the whole design will have to be changed, and both the ground glass used in focusing and the film will have to be moved very close to the eyepiece of the microscope.

It is to be regretted that more specific instructions can not be given for exposure. The variables present are far too numerous to make such data possible. There is the matter of film brand and type, quality of the microscope, nature of the specimen—that is, density—degree of illumination, etc. By and large, however, it may be said that for amateur work at least, there is no need of any special film except in cases where advanced work in color might be attempted or where filters were to be employed. Such cases might bring up the matter of orthochromatic versus panchromatic. The very nature of the work, however, especially as it relates to the use of 35 mm. film, does make fine-grain development strongly advisable if not imperative.

About the only thing that may be done to settle once and for all the matter of exposure is to set about taking pictures. A specimen is set in place and exposed, say, three times. We might use three seconds for the first, four seconds for the second, and five seconds for the third. We take care also to mark each plate or film holder, so that the results in relation to time may be examined after development. With these as a guide, we shall know much more about timing when the next photomicrographs are taken.

There is another, less often practised method of taking photomicrographs, which employs any kind of camera—miniature, Kodak, or Brownie (box). Careful manipulation will bring reasonably good results. This method does not require that the lens be removed from the camera, nor is it necessary to remove the back and replace it with a piece of ground glass for focusing. Any camera, regardless of type, cost, power or size is used "as is." It follows that for convenience, if nothing else, the smaller the camera the less trouble will be had mounting it. Consequently, cameras employing 35 mm. film are nice for such use. The film is also economical to use, and we may avoid the expense of a projector by rigging up a little magnifying device with a small lamp. Ideas along this line may be had by a trip to a photographic supply shop, where such devices are on display.

The ideal arrangement for a connection between a miniature 35 mm. camera and a microscope is illustrated in Fig. 25. This calls for metal working, however, that may be beyond the shop facilities and the skill of the amateur. Of course, if the worker is clever, he may build one from wood, cardboard, or even from the metal in a tin can. The last will require soldering, but that is not a difficult matter. Dimensions will depend upon the diameter of the lens of the camera and the diameter of the eyepiece of the microscope. A small ring rests inside the attachment, and the article, regardless of the materials used in its construction, should be painted dull black inside and out. A cable release for the shutter should be used to prevent vibration, although it is also possible to

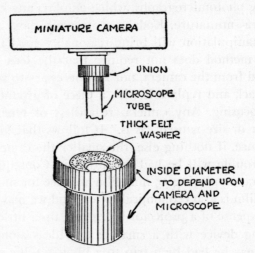

FIG. 25. A metal connecter for use with miniature camera and microscope.

dispense with the use of the shutter by turning the light on and off instead. The latter method is perhaps best because this makes vibration only a remote possibility.

To use our equipment we place the specimen to be photographed on the stage of the microscope and focus in the accustomed manner. When we are sure that we have a fine image, we are ready for the placement of the camera, but if it is of the focusing type, we must first adjust the focus to infinity—that is, for the long distance view. This done, the camera is set in place and the picture is taken. Should a box camera be used, the procedure is the same, although it will be clear that in any case the lens of the camera used must be set the same distance above the lens in the eyepiece of the microscope as the eye of the observer.

Certain subjects photographed with this equipment will require filters, either green or blue. For instance, when diatoms are being recorded, blue filters are often employed. These can be of the ordinary photographic type, and they may be placed between the eyepiece of the microscope and the lens of the camera.

8

Smoke in Your Eyes

A PHENOMENON of matter long studied by physicists all over the world has been called the Brownian movement. A Scot named Robert Brown discovered the effect well over one hundred years ago, and much has been said, written, and done about it since those days. The subject is still a very live one, and it can be made most fascinating for amateur microscopists, as was demonstrated some time ago by Mr. George H. Parsons, one of the leaders in the hobby.

The Brownian movement relates to the movement of tiny particles called colloids when they are suspended in solutions and in the air. What we propose to do here is to watch the Brownian movement of the tiny particles in tobacco smoke.

It is a curious thing, this Brownian affair. For instance, in the case of smoke, the particles behave as though they were constantly being pushed around by invisible jostlers. We see a particle lazily moving along in a perfectly orderly manner when it suddenly lurches into headlong flight in *any* direction. There is nothing predictable either about when or where the particle will be struck or in what direction it will be caused to move. Particles are violently shoved first one way and then another, zigzagging across the field of vision in a drunken manner.

In the case of colloidal smoke particles, movement is closely tied up with the kinetic theory of gases. It is assumed, and with ample reason, that the tiny bits of solid matter in the smoke are being pushed and shoved around by molecules, themselves made active by the effect of heat. Watching this effect can prove fascinating. However, we shall have to seek the help of a little device which has been perfected by the aforementiond Mr. Parsons. This is easy to make, and many interesting and pleasurable hours may be wrung from it. What it really amounts to is nothing more or less than a smoke chamber arranged with special illumination.

Inasmuch as the device for the study and observation of the Brownian movement will probably be used on a microscope without a condenser, a condenser lens must be incorporated. This must be of a very short focus. However, the prospective builder should not permit this to change his plans. The special short-focus lens may be obtained at the local chain store in the form of a glass marble. The usual bag of marbles obtainable from this source includes a few tinted a pale yellow, and these will do very nicely for the work at hand.

The principle of our smoke magnifier is that of permitting tobacco smoke to enter a small box under proper conditions of lighting. The box is equipped with a glass top, and the microscope objective is

brought close to this. The little box or chamber is
made of bristol board of the sort used for painted
signs. This should be a dull black on the inside.
The assembly may be accomplished with the kind of
cement used in the construction of model airplanes.

The piece of cardboard carrying the lens measures
1½ x 1¼ inches, and the lens or marble is inserted

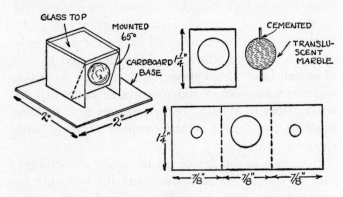

Fig. 26. The construction details for the ingenious device
used in seeing the colloidal particles in smoke.

in a 9/16 inch hole. Model airplane cement is used
again, this time being smeared around the joint between the marble and the cardboard. This member
of the smoke chamber is then set aside to permit the
cement to set. In the meantime, we proceed to cut
and assemble the remainder of the container. The
three other sides (it will be seen from the drawing
that the lens mount forms one) are cut from a strip
of the cardboard measuring 3 inches long by ⅞ inch
wide. Using the white side, we draw three pencil

lines ⅞ inch apart, and these are carefully scored with a knife. We must take care not to score so deeply as to cut through the paper. The surplus cardboard is removed by cutting completely through the third line.

In the center section of the piece just cut we find the exact center. This is easily done by drawing diagonal lines that intersect. At the point of intersection we draw a circle about ⅜ inch in diameter. This is cut out carefully with the point of a very sharp knife. The ⅛ inch holes shown may be cut with an ordinary paper punch. These are used in filling the chamber with smoke, and they are kept closed with small wooden plugs or corks.

After the three sides have been set in place, the lens-bearing member is cemented in position. This must be set in at exactly 65° and in the manner shown in our drawing. It will also be noted from the drawing that the box is provided with a cardboard base and that this may be cemented in position. The object here is merely that of supplying a projecting surface that can be engaged by the spring clips on the microscope stage. The top of the box is made up of a piece of microscope slide also cemented in place. Any other kind of glass will not serve because of optical imperfections which introduce serious distortion.

The use of the smoke chamber is simple enough. A *clear* electric bulb is placed in our lamp house or illuminator, and a beam is thrown through the marble. After the light passes through the yellow-tinted marble, it will become a cone of illumination, the apex of which, if the dimensions in the drawing have been followed carefully and the marble is exactly 5⁄8 inch in diameter, will just reach the top of the opposite wall. Of course, it will also be necessary not only to place a clear glass bulb in the microscope lamp but also to place a piece of cardboard with a small hole in it over the face of the lamp, so that a beam will be formed.

Smoke is admitted to the chamber by means of the little plugs. The chamber is then placed on the stage of the microscope and held in position through the agency of the spring clips. The objective is brought down to within 1/16 inch of the glass top; use a piece of cardboard here if necessary to prevent actual collision between the lens and the glass; the light is switched on, and focusing adjustments are made.

We should now see (at the highest magnification possible with our instrument) the tiny particles of smoke, much like dust particles in a sunbeam. These particles, however, are many times smaller than floating dust particles, and they will perform quite differently; rather dramatically, indeed, if we have an eye for interesting physical effects. These particles are so small that they will be knocked helter-skelter by mere collision with molecules. Soon, however, and for reasons still not quite understood, the scene will quiet down and our little particles will flow about in the air of the chamber much like ordinary dust particles. When the scene becomes stale, we merely recharge the chamber with more smoke.

9

Home-Made Micro-Projectors

ONE great disadvantage of the microscope is the
limitation of vision. Ordinarily, only one person at a time can see the specimen under observation. Projection equipment can be had in manufactured form, but it is expensive—far too expensive to
suit the modest pocket-book of the average amateur.
Fortunately, the optical principles involved are so
simple as to make the home construction of such
equipment come easily within the skill of most hobbyists, and there will be described below two types
of projectors, one for great magnification and one for
family use.

The projector for family use is particularly easy to
make. Aside from the ground glass required for the
screen, the bill of materials can probably be filled
without stirring out of the house. Ground glass may
be had for a few cents a square foot at any photographic supply house.

The box (see Fig. 27) can be assembled either
from heavy cardboard or from light (⅜ inch) plywood. If cardboard is used, cloth adhesive tape and
model airplane cement will be found most useful in
effecting assembly. The mirror can be held in place

in the same manner. The ground glass should not be larger than 8 x 10 inches, and the projector box does not need to be over 14 inches long. The image cast on the glass will be sufficiently large to be seen by a small group.

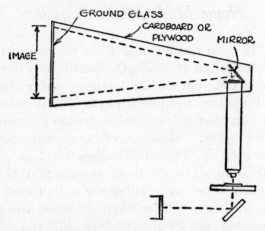

FIG. 27. A simple projector that casts images on a ground glass screen. The case may be made of cardboard or plywood.

Another glance at Fig. 27 reveals the presence of a small mirror mounted at 45° over the eyepiece of the microscope. This may be held to a dowel with sealing wax, the dowel being long enough to pass through the portion of the box directly over the microscope. Inasmuch as it is important that the mirror be adjusted at exactly 45°, such adjustment may be arrived at and preserved by this method.

Unless an exceptionally powerful source of illumination is used with this equipment, it will be neces-

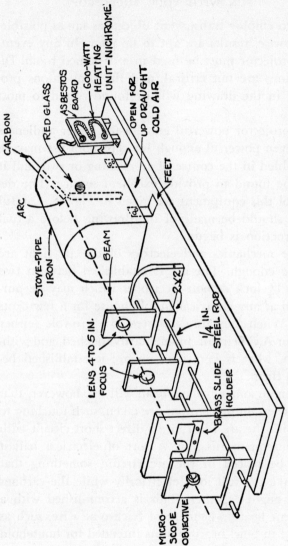

Fig. 28. A powerful projector intended for small lecture-hall use. Here the source of illumination is an arc light.

sary to employ transparent objects as far as possible. Otherwise, results are apt to be poor. In any event, the projector must be used in a darkened room. Dimensions are not critical, and the proportions provided in the drawing will be found suited to most cases.

A projector powerful enough for larger audiences and even powerful enough for classroom use may be assembled in the course of an evening or two, and it will be found to provide excellent service. The details of this equipment are given in Fig. 28. Careful study should be made of the drawing before actual construction is begun.

The mechanics and electrics of the arc light are simple enough. The arc is established between two ⅜ or ¼ inch carbon electrodes which may be purchased at any electrical supply house for a few cents each. When they are connected to a 110-volt (either D.C. or A.C.) circuit, momentarily touched, and withdrawn, what is known as an arc is established between them.

Even an amateur electrician will see, however, that unless certain precautions are taken, such touching to establish the arc will cause a direct short circuit with its consequent disaster. A sort of electrical ballast must be placed in the arc circuit, something that can take the full load electrically while the carbons are brought together. This is accomplished with a 600-watt heating element of Nichrome wire, such as is used in bowl heating units intended for household purposes. If such a heater is available, the heating unit may be taken out and temporarily employed with the projector. No harm to the unit will result in its employment on the projector.

Electric arc lamps require a great deal of current while they are in operation, and for this reason ample electrical facilities will have to be installed on our

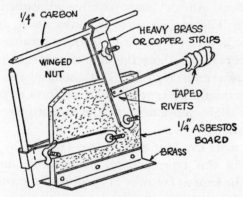

FIG. 29. The mechanical details of the home-constructed arc intended for use with the micro-projector.

little machine. Connections should be made with No. 14 insulated wire, and special care should be taken to establish adequate connections with the carbons. If this is not done, excessive heat will develop at these connections and secondary arcs of smaller size will be set up. These will sooner or later melt the metal in contact with the carbons, and a great deal of trouble is likely to result. Contact with the carbons must be established over a comparatively wide area and should be kept as tight as possible. So far as the specifications of the arc light equipment are concerned, they will be found quite simple.

Inasmuch as the successful operation of this projector depends almost entirely upon the arc lamp, it is thought best to cover this point thoroughly. Few people have ever had much experience with such equipment. An arc lamp requires adjustment periodically. The carbon actually burns away, and the distance between the carbons becomes greater until a point is reached where the flow of excessive current will blow even heavy fuses. The distance between the carbons should be kept as nearly uniform as possible by the slight movement of the carbons every few moments.

One more caution: great heat is radiated by a light source of this type, and all inflammable materials should be kept as far away as possible. Otherwise they will be scorched or set afire.

Considerable liberty may be taken with the other mechanical details, provided the general dimensions are preserved as far as possible. Of course, the lens system must be established as indicated, but even here considerable latitude is possible. The small condenser lenses may vary in focal length between 4 and 5 inches, and their mounting does not need to follow the directions given, as long as they are firmly fixed in place. Such lenses may be had from photographic supply shops. These people usually stock such articles or they can be obtained from their wholesale suppliers.

The only other lens used comes from the microscope itself and is borrowed for the purpose. This is a low-priced objective, and we must be careful in mounting it to see that the threads are not in any way damaged or fouled. Each time the lenses are taken out or replaced in the microscope, we make a very careful inspection to check for pieces of grit. Indeed, it will do no harm to wipe the threads off with a clean cloth each time the objective is replaced in the microscope.

Certain purely mechanical precautions are necessary if our little machine is to function smoothly. It will be noted, for instance, that both the condenser and the objective lenses are adjustable along the $\frac{1}{4}$ inch rods. The builder should provide for movement without binding. This is a mere matter of the mechanical accuracy of the holes drilled in the boards carrying the lenses. If they are drilled on a drill press, they will offer no trouble at all. On the other hand, if they are carelessly drilled askew by means of a breast drill, trouble will be had in moving them along the rods.

The housing for the arc is absolutely essential. It may be bent into shape from light sheet-iron. Lining with asbestos would not be amiss, although it is not strictly necessary. Due to the need for constant inspection of the arc light, a peep-hole must be included in the side of the lamp house at a point where it will be directly opposite the light source. Some attempt should be made to shield the eyes and make good inspection possible. Merely peeking in through a hole at the arc will be of little use because of the blinding radiance. Very little can be seen in this manner. The hole must be covered with a very dark red or blue glass.

The operation of the micro-projector is simple enough. Obviously, it must be used in darkness, and the projections should be thrown on a white sheet. It is urged that we have some rehearsal before we make the mistake of gathering friends for our first demonstration. Perhaps a full hour or more will be needed for making the necessary optical adjustments and repeating them so that we will become more or less expert in doing this. First, attention is focused on the lamp house and the proper adjustment of the light source after the arc has been struck. The arc must line up with the center of the condenser and objective lens. Otherwise, optical efficiency will be so low as to defeat any clear projection. The condenser lens nearest the objective should be moved until a bright and sharply defined circle of light falls upon the back of the board which carries the slide to be shown.

The location of the arc can be shifted up and down by the movement of the two carbons. Sidewise shifts can also be made, through the medium of the wood screw shown in the drawing.

The sheet or screen (bead movie screen is excellent if it is available) is set about five feet from the objective lens. Once the rear adjustments have been made, the objective is adjusted until the image is clearly defined on the wall.

A great deal of fun and entertainment may be had with this little outfit in the actual projection of living creatures. For this we purchase a microscope slide with a depression ground in the center. This is laid flat on our table and filled to the top with stagnant water that we know holds a large amount of microscopic life. A clean cover-glass is now placed

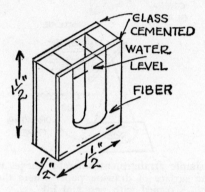

FIG. 30. A simple cooling cell for use with the arc projector.

over this and rubber bands are slipped over the two glasses at each end to hold the combination together. The result is placed in the slide holder in the same manner as any other slide.

It might be that too much heat would reach the specimens used for projection. In that event, we should constuct a water cooling cell and set it up between the two condenser lenses. A great deal of the heat carried by the beam of light will be absorbed by this arrangement. The details of this cooling cell are shown in Fig. 30.

If a cover-glass is mounted in a small brass frame like that illustrated in Fig. 31, this arrangement may be used to project objects on paper, where they may

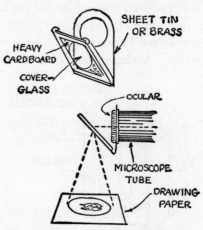

SHEET TIN OR BRASS

HEAVY CARDBOARD

COVER-GLASS

OCULAR

MICROSCOPE TUBE

DRAWING PAPER

FIG. 31. A simple arrangement whereby images may be reflected to the surface of drawing paper where they may be copied with pen and ink.

be drawn or traced for the microscopist's note-book. For this purpose, the microscope is mounted horizontally. The frame carrying the cover-glass should be mounted at 45°.

10

Still More Fun With These Accessories

THE optical shops dealing in microscope equipment hold many prized pieces, things that the
beginner, once he masters the essentials of his hobby,
will be wanting. Most of them will be beyond his
reach financially, but there is some consolation in
the fact that not a small number of these things can
be duplicated in the home workshop. They will not
be chromium plated or supplied with an expensive
finish. They will work, however, and work well.

The aggressive pursuit of our hobby will probably
bring us to a point where we shall wish to share some
of the marvelous things we are seeing with a brother,
sister, or son. The microscope does not lend itself to
double views, although, surprisingly enough, a few
hours spent at our work-bench and the use of rather
common materials will provide a "twosome" arrangement whereby our most exciting views may be shared.

By the use of the device about to be described, the
light from a microscope as it appears at the eyepiece
is split and equally divided between two persons. The
device really amounts to a second eyepiece super-
imposed upon the one already in use.

The cost of the bill of materials is not excessive in

view of the new facilities that will be made available. It will be necessary to purchase another eyepiece or ocular, complete with tube, from the maker of the microscope we are using. Inasmuch as most of us will be using a modest amateur instrument, this

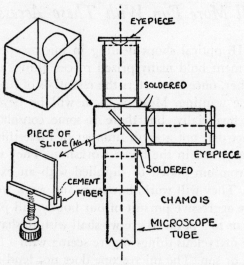

FIG. 32. The general construction of the "double-seeing" device intended for use with any kind of microscope.

cost does not need to run high. In most cases not more than three to four dollars need be paid.

The impossibility of providing actual measurements in the drawing, Fig. 32, will be understood. These must depend upon the make of microscope to which the accessory is to be applied. However, before we set out on the construction of the device, let us gather in a bit of information on the operation of our gadget. Assistance in understanding this will be gained from the drawing. Light moves upward until it strikes the glass slide mounted at an angle of 45°. This, let it be known now, before we forget, is a No. 1 microscope slide, the thinnest made. Inasmuch as the slide is not treated in any manner but left clear, part of the light (about half, we hope) coming from the object being viewed will pass on upward to the vertical eyepiece. The other half will be reflected off at 45° and pass through the ocular mounted horizontally.

The ingenious worker should have little trouble making a device of this kind. Should he have trouble in obtaining metal tubing of the correct size, he may turn to making it himself by wrapping thin sheet metal around a dowel of the right size and soldering the seam. Or, if this method does not appeal to him, he may set about building his tubes up with paper wrapped around a dowel in a laminated fashion. Plenty of glue should be used, and the paper should not be wound so tightly that the dowel can not be removed from the tube. It may also be that tubes of the right kind are available at the local stationery store. If paper is used, the cement employed in the fabrication of model airplanes will be found exceptionally useful. The builder, whatever he uses in the construction of his accessory, must be sure to cover the inside with some sort of jet black varnish or paint.

Fig. 33 illustrates the details of another gadget, more simple than the last but extremely useful.

Oftentimes we shall be wanting to view the entire body of an insect with a low-powered objective. Turning him over repeatedly will be a bit irksome and time wasting. What we need is some sort of gadget for the purpose. With the one shown, the victim is impaled on the end of a small needle and set in such

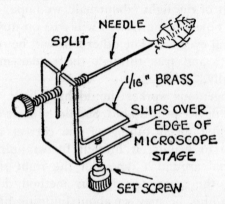

Fig. 33. A device used in the examination of insects and the like, where whole surfaces are to be looked at with comparatively low power.

a manner under the objective that he is turned as on a spit. This is much more convenient than attempting to roll the specimen over and over on the stage of the microscope.

The whole matter of the manipulation of specimens becomes one of considerable moment for the untrained microscopist. Both distance and speed are magnified with a microscope, and where one is engaged in viewing a specimen at high power, one is likely to become very much annoyed at one's own clumsiness. Even the expert worker can do very little better. It just does not lie within the range of human muscular coördination to produce controlled micro-movements, and for this reason even the old hand turns to mechanical manipulation.

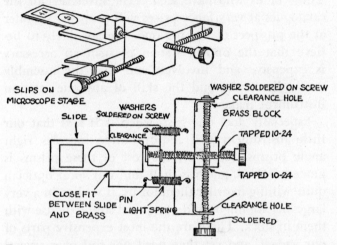

FIG. 34. A simple home-made micro-manipulator used in moving slides in two directions.

A glance at Fig. 34 will reveal the details of a simple, home-made micro-manipulator that can be produced by the home mechanic using simple tools and simple equipment. It will not function with the smoothness and accuracy of the devices manufactured for this purpose, but, on the other hand, neither will it cost as much.

Perhaps as the amateur warms to the lure of the microscope he will have more and more occasion to lament the fact that microscopy at large, at least as far as the amateur is concerned, is pretty much a one-eyed affair. This does not need to remain so if the hobbyist has enough daring to undertake the construction of a binocular eyepiece for his instrument. Those of us who have seen them advertised in the catalogues at very fancy prices will probably shudder at the prospect of making one. We are likely to believe that the optical system of such an accessory is expensive and involved and that the assembly would lie far beyond the skill of any one save an instrument maker.

Especially does one gasp when it is said that our little instrument will require three isosceles right angle prisms. However, the cost of these prisms is modest indeed, and we shall find our local optician quite willing to order them for us. If we live in a very large city we might find an optical supply house with them in stock. These are the most expensive parts of our gadget, and yet they need not cost over several dollars—that is, for the lot of them.

The prisms should not measure over one inch on the right-angle legs nor should they be smaller than one-half inch. Thus we see that considerable latitude is allowed here. The difference in price of the pieces will be small, however.

Examination of the drawings (Figs. 35 and 36) will reveal the method of mounting the prisms. Tiny wooden or fiber triangles may be used for the purpose. Perhaps it would be advisable to cut these first and to cement the prisms to them, inasmuch as twenty-four hours of drying will be required. During this time, the builder can be busy finishing the rest of the instrument.

The builder will note that the wooden or fiber triangles carrying the prisms are drilled and counter-

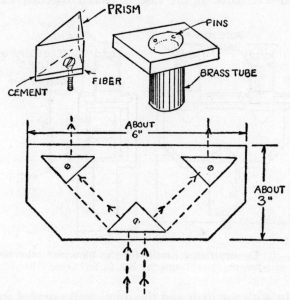

FIG. 35. The principle of the binocular instruments together with details for mounting the prisms and lens tube.

sunk for a machine screw. This feature should not be forgotten: otherwise, the prisms might be cemented in place first. Not only should these holes be drilled and countersunk, but the screws used should be set in position.

Any good commercial cement may be used, or we

may turn to water-glass. In any event, the cement
should be given twenty-four hours to set.

The box itself may be assembled from cigar-box
wood, and the cement used by model airplane workers may be employed in its assembly along with
cigar-box nails. If the case is tacked together care-

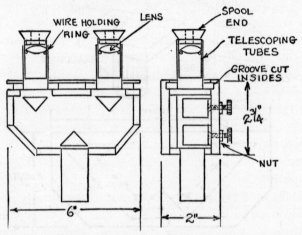

FIG. 36. Constructional details for the binocular microscope
attachment. Dimensions are not in any sense critical.

fully, with the nails and the joints well smeared with
the cement, a very rigid and strong construction will
result.

Each eyepiece of the instrument must be equipped
with a small portrait lens which may be had cheaply
enough from a photographic dealer. These should
be about one inch in diameter, and they will have to
be mounted as shown in the drawing. Of course,
such mounting simply means that we shall have to

search for the telescoping metal tubes until they are found. This, however, should not be too difficult. It will be noted that a small ring of copper wire is soldered to the inside of each a short distance down from the end. This forms a seat for each lens. The eyepiece can be cut from a wooden thread spool.

The builder will also note that the eyepieces are so arranged that they can be moved sidewise for the purpose of optical adjustments. This will be quite necessary if the instrument is to be used efficiently. It should also be noted that the inside of the whole case and the tubes can be rendered non-reflecting by the use of some sort of dead-black material.

If the case itself is made of cigar-box wood, and a good finish is to be produced, it will be necessary to employ a good grain-filler and plenty of careful sand-papering before the final finish is applied, which should be a dull or semi-dull black.

The metal capping tube at the bottom of the instrument, which is large enough to fit over the eyepiece of the microscope upon which the device is to be used, must be supplied with a chamois lining to prevent damage to the finish on our microscope. This may be cemented inside the cap.

When the device is set in place, some rather careful adjustments will be needed to set it in optical operation. This will be related to the adjustment of both the eyepieces (up and down) and the prisms (turning on axis). Perhaps a half-hour or so of fussing will make the instrument available for use, and much fun will be had by using two eyes in place of one.

Indeed, the worker will thereafter want to use his new equipment all the time, and there is no reason why this should not be done. Few are the hobbyists who learn to keep both eyes open during the use of the microscope. This is supposed to be the proper

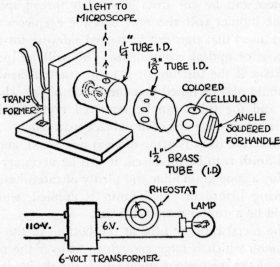

FIG. 37. A small microscope illuminator easy to make and efficient in use.

way to manipulate an instrument, but it is most difficult to acquire the knack. Hence, the instrument described herewith will be found helpful in gaining a better view of all objects.

As we advance into our hobby, a time will come when we shall fail to be satisfied with things as we first used them: we shall be seeking greater perfection all the way down the line. As likely as not, many of us will become dissatisfied with our illumination and will want to achieve more professional stand-ards.

The little illuminator illustrated in Fig. 37 can be assembled from a bit of metal tubing, a small lamp,

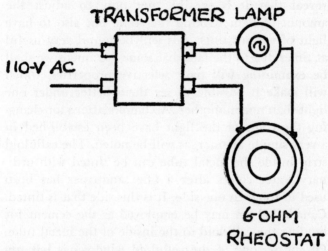

FIG. 38. The electrical connections for the transformer, rheo-stat, and lamp.

and a few odds and ends. Current may be had either from a battery of a few dry cells or from a small bell-ringing transformer. These transformers are sup-plied in different voltages, and we shall therefore have to be careful to adjust the voltage of the lamp we purchase to the voltage of the transformer we use. The voltage of the transformer should be a bit higher than the voltage of the lamp; otherwise, the lamp will not burn at its rated brilliancy. On the other hand, the voltage of the transformer can be considerably above the voltage of the lamp, and a rheostat can be placed in the circuit (as shown in Fig. 38) to keep the voltage adjusted to a proper level.

Examination of the drawing of the little lamp will reveal that it is possible not only to adjust the amount of light striking the scene but also to have light of various tints: this will be found very useful at times due to the fact that some specimens we shall be examining will have selective properties, which will make it possible to see them better under one light than under another. Accommodations for changing the color of the light have been established in a very simple manner, as will be noted. The celluloid strip inside the metal tube can be tinted with ordinary water colors after a fine sandpaper has been used to roughen one side. It is this side that is tinted. Canada balsam may be employed as the cement for holding the celluloid to the inside of the metal tube. Of course, one of the celluloid windows is left uncolored, but this section of the celluloid is also sandpapered so as to provide diffusion for the light coming from the bulb below.

The apertures in the one piece of tubing may vary all the way from 1/16 inch in diameter to 1/4 inch in diameter. The holes in the color screen arrangement should all be 1/4 to 3/8 inch, so they will be sure to be at least the same size or larger than the holes in the other member.

As they move along in their hobby, most microscopists will wish to increase their facilities for the

examination of opaque surfaces. These are rather
difficult to view with ordinary microscopic equipment. What is needed, as we shall sooner or later
discover, is what is known as a vertical illuminator.
If reference is made to Fig. 39 the details of a simple
and extremely useful accessory will be found. The

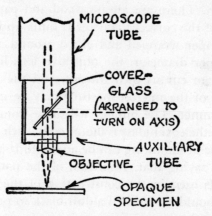

FIG. 39. A home-made device used in the examination of
opaque surfaces.

operation of the illuminator is based on the fact that
a thin piece of glass such as a cover-slide will partially
reflect light and partially pass it when it is placed in
a beam at an angle of 45°.

Further study of the drawing of Fig. 39 will reveal that the ordinary objective lens of the microscope is removed from the end of the tube and set
up in business in a new position and that a microscope cover-glass is placed between it and the objective.

Actual dimensions and details of construction of this vertical illuminator can not be given because the construction of microscopes varies a great deal. Of course, the ingenious worker will not permit this absence of data to deter him. Nor need his inability to work in metal, because of the absence of proper tools, stop him. There are always wood and paper left. If a tube of the correct diameter is built up from laminated paper wrapped and glued around a dowel of the proper diameter, the objective lens holder may be used to cut its own threads, and the threads in the end of the microscope tube may be used in the same manner. The builder will note from the drawing that the cover-glass is mounted in such a way that the angle of mounting can be adjusted. It almost goes without saying that, regardless of the nature of the materials used in the construction of the thing, the inside should be finished a dull black to prevent conflicting reflections.

Still another accessory is shown in Fig. 40, where the details of a general utility device are given. This can be employed for holding auxiliary condensing lenses, diffusing screens, and filters. The heavy wire employed for the construction of the standard may be taken from a coat hanger. The thin sheet steel used for the filter holder may be gathered from any tin can. Filters used do not need to be any larger than 2 x 2. They may be purchased from any optical supply house, and they are not expensive. A good light diffuser may be cut from an ordinary piece of ground glass such as is used for photographic purposes. The condensing lens may be any ordinary reading-glass obtainable at a chain store. Here optical perfection is not required, since no images will be viewed through this member.

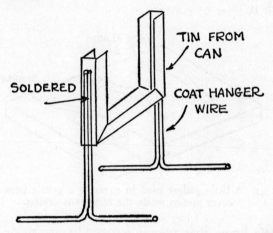

FIG. 40. A useful accessory for holding filters and the like.

When mounting specimens on slides, the worker will probably welcome some assistance in the form of a little gadget that exerts a gentle pressure on cover-glasses while the cement is setting. One does not want to stand about holding slides between the fingers while this is taking place. Hence, our little gadget (Fig. 41), made completely of wood save for the springs, is made to accommodate three slides. The pressure on the cover-glasses must be very light, else it is apt to break them.

The little device about to be described really has nothing whatever to do with microscopy as such.

Rather, it is a gadget that must be used in connection with a microscope, and it will be of particular interest to those who dabble in amateur photography. It is easily made, and not a little fun may be had with it.

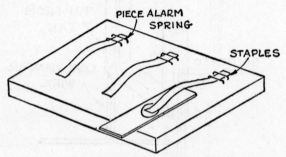

FIG. 41. A little gadget used in exerting a gentle pressure on cover glasses while the cement is drying.

We know that photomicrographs are made from magnified objects. The device at hand (Fig. 42) is used to make microphotographs—ultra-small pictures. In this instance, the microscope is used as a reducer rather than as an enlarger. When photomicrographs are taken, the unexposed negative is placed above the objective. When the microphotograph is taken, the negative material (unexposed) is placed below the objective. The developed negative representing the picture we wish to have reduced is placed above the eyepiece and projected downward through the lens system.

Fig. 42 will present the details with sufficient clarity for construction. The builder, however, is warned here and now that the opal glass must be employed and that ground glass will prove quite useless as a substitute. Since this is so, one does not have to care

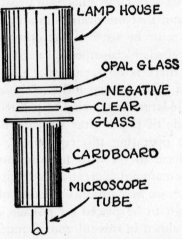

LAMP HOUSE

OPAL GLASS

NEGATIVE

CLEAR GLASS

CARDBOARD

MICROSCOPE TUBE

FIG. 42. The general arrangement of a device used in making microphotographs with the camera.

much about the electric bulb in the lamp house. This may be either frosted or unfrosted, as long as it is about 40 watts capacity.

An examination of the equipment as presented in the drawing will reveal that the negative to be reduced is held flat between the clear glass and the opal glass. Unless we wish to construct a very bulky and awkward camera, we should not plan to use negatives over 2¼ x 2¼ inches, although there is no reason why a small section of any negative can not be picked out, masked off, and "inverted," as we might say.

Any one with any photographic sense must see, however, that very clear, fine-grain negatives must be employed and that fine-grain film and fine-grain development must be used at the other end. With a reasonably good microscope and a good negative to start with, there is no reason why pictures can not be made as small as five millimeters square. More ordinary "de-largements" may be printed directly on a good grade of paper after we have had some experience in operating this equipment. The experience will have to do with focusing and exposure. Once this is mastered, a great deal of fun may be had. For instance, we may produce pictures of our friends small enough to be placed on postage stamps.

Focusing down in this sub-zone is much more difficult than focusing for ordinary enlargements. A good hand magnifying glass with a power of 7 or 8 will be quite helpful—indeed, imperative at the lower limits. Of course, film in the sizes that we shall be using it rules out heavy expense.

Fig. 43 shows how a slip of film may be placed in a black paper jacket with a window. After each exposure is made, the film is pulled forward a bit to bring up a fresh piece.

The lamp house of the microphotographic camera is made from a three-pound can used for cottonseed oil shortening. A square 2 x 2 inches is cut out of one end and a round hole cut in the cover to permit the entrance of the cord. The socket may be soldered to the cover.

There is no reason why the lower half of the camera can not be made up of soft pine and bristol board. The bristol board used should be dull black

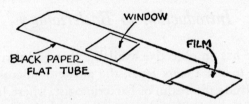

FIG. 43. Black paper tubing with a window is used with the microphotograph camera.

on one side and white on the other, the black being used inside. Using wood and cardboard in place of metal will lighten the attachment a great deal, so that it may be placed on the microscope without special brackets. It should be pointed out that the entire interior of the lower portion should be made a dull black to eliminate unwanted reflections.

11

Introduction to Bacteriology

IF he has an objective available that will carry him up to the 1,000x level, the amateur microscopist may invade the realm of bacteriologist, where he will find many a thrill and much that is of absorbing interest. Aside from the moderately powered microscope, there is nothing that will cost any more than a few cents to construct. Of course, if one is not satisfied with home fabrications and wishes to equip his laboratory with professional devices, the cost may be excessive. It may be said here and now that the devices about to be described will perform efficiently and that they will also bear up in service.

We can not, however, hope to cover the actual subject of bacteriology here beyond a description of the equipment that will be needed to generate germ hordes. Any local library will yield at least one book devoted to the topic, and, if possible, the beginner should turn to Jordan's *General Bacteriology*. Here will be found not only a great deal of data relating to the identification of bacteria but also full directions for generating all the more common varieties. The work can be utterly fascinating, and it also is known to be inexhaustible. One could spend a full lifetime merely reviewing the work that others have done.

The amateur microscopist, turning to the study of bacteria, must learn to grow the "little beasties," as van Leeuwenhoek called them. To grow them, he must have an incubator—nothing more or less than a box where an even temperature around 90° C. prevails. It should be kept in mind at the outset, also, that we must know not only how to generate germs but how to kill them. Control is the point. In many instances, we shall be wanting to sterilize equipment. In other instances, we put a culture to work in a medium and set it going with life-giving heat so that our little bugs will thrive and multiply. If we do not sterilize properly, then our little bugs will get all mixed up, and we shall have the devil's own time with our identifications and classifications.

An oven ideally suited to sterilization can be assembled in a few hours' time, using an empty five-gallon oil can. This should first be rinsed out with gasoline to remove the last traces of oil; then, after the opening is cut for the door, as illustrated in Fig. 44, we may give the inside another thorough washing, this time with hot, soapy water. This should dissolve away the last traces of grease.

As we shall note by another reference to Fig. 44, the piece cut out from the tin can can not be used for the door because it is too small. We shall need a piece of sheet metal about $\frac{1}{2}$ inch larger than the opening all the way around.

Two small brass hinges are used for the door, and

these may be held in place with small machine screws, with rivets, or by soldering. Some sort of catch should also be installed to keep the door closed. If we look around at the hardware store, we can probably find just the ticket for this sort of thing.

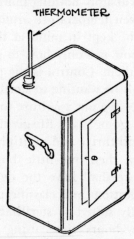

THERMOMETER

FIG. 44. The simple oven made with a five-gallon can.

The oven is finished by installing a 200° Centigrade thermometer in a perforated cork, the latter being large enough to act as a bung or stopper for the hole in the top of the can. The two insulated handles installed on the sides of the oven will permit us to lift it from the gas stove while it is hot, thereby saving time. In actual service, the oven may be placed on a small gas plate in our laboratory. In any event, the flame can be adjusted so that heat beyond the range of the thermometer will not be used. It must be recalled that 100° C. is equivalent to 212° F. or the boiling point of water.

The steam sterilizer used by bacteriologists costs as much as a good microscope if professional standards are required. However, there is no occasion for the amateur to insist upon professional standards. All he needs is a five-gallon steel drum such as is supplied

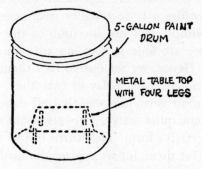

5-GALLON PAINT DRUM

METAL TABLE TOP WITH FOUR LEGS

FIG. 45. A steam sterilizer may be made from a five-gallon paint or white lead drum.

with white lead. Most painters have several such drums in their workshops, and fifty cents is a lot to pay for one of them.

A four-legged metal table of some sort (see Fig. 45) is made to fit inside the drum, and the dishes or slides to be sterilized are placed on this. Water is placed in the bottom and the whole set over an open gas burner turned low. The water should be brought to a boil and the cover set gently in place—not forced down. As the steam pressure rises inside, the cover will be lifted, and excess pressure will not develop.

Media must be sterilized in this steam chamber on three successive days. One half-hour on each occasion will be quite enough. However, the worker must make sure that he brings the water to a boil each time and that it remains at a boil for at least half an hour. The first heat treatment is bound to dispatch all the purely vegetative forms of life in the media. The spores, however, are not dealt with so easily: they will require a little tougher treatment. In this form, they simply will not succumb to the temperatures that we are able to develop with our modest equipment. Hence, we set out to fool them. If they are left unmolested for a day or two, they, thinking perhaps in their germ-like way that all dangers have passed, become quite active. They set about changing into the vegetative form. That turns out to be a serious mistake for them, for we replace the media in the steam drum and the new forms go the way of all germ flesh. Another steam bath on the third day is pretty sure to provide the experimenter with a medium that will be quite free from all forms of germ invasion.

Now for the incubator: here we shall have to be a bit more careful, and the materials that we shall be using will be a bit more expensive. The incubator is nothing more or less than a hothouse in which we rear our various forms of germs. The temperatures developed must be neither too hot nor too cold but just right. If they reach too high a point, all our little beasties will be killed off, and our slides will show us nothing for our lengthy labors. Even temperatures call for automatic temperature control by means of the thermostat. That will sound bad to most of us; it sounds like real money. Not so. As we shall soon see, this gadget can be very easily made and need not cost over a few pennies if we are at all clever with tools.

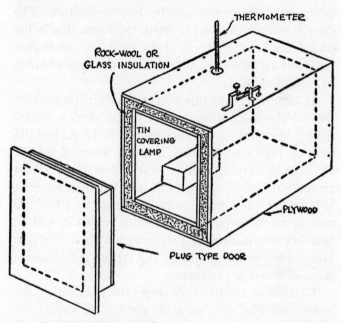

FIG. 46. This simple incubator does not need to cost the amateur bacteriologist over two dollars.

The oven or container should be made first, for the thermostat is installed in this. The incubator should not be over a foot square inside and a foot three inches on the outside. It will be noted from Fig. 46 that in making the incubator we really make two boxes of plywood, telescoping one within the other, the intervening space being filled with some sort of insulating material like glass wool. A non-inflammable insulator would be best. It will be seen that this should be installed in the back or bottom of the larger box before the smaller one is inserted. The door is made with double walls, the insulation being placed inside. The details of the work are not important, so long as we are able to keep the heat where it belongs: inside.

As a check against our automatic temperature control we also use a thermometer in this device. It may have a low reading, because there will be no need to develop high temperatures. Indeed, some of the life we shall be helping will be so sensitive to the higher temperatures that we shall kill it rather than generate it if we are not careful. Some of our germs like darkness better than light, and for this reason it will be best to cover our heating element, which is a 60-watt lamp. This is installed with the right kind of socket screwed down in the corner.

To make our automatic temperature control equipment (see Fig. 47), we shall need some small glass tubing, with a bore about ⅛ inch in diameter. It will be noted that this glass tubing has four bends and that the end is closed. This calls for a bit of work over a gas flame, and it also calls for bending without collapsing. If the tube collapses, and the walls become welded together during the operation, the whole unit will be rendered useless. The secret lies in not permitting the tube to reach too high a temperature while the heat is applied and in doing the bending gradually. The tube is moved to right and left through the gas flame while the heating is done, so that the heat will not be concentrated over one spot. With a little care and without practice a cautious tinker should be able to come through with flying

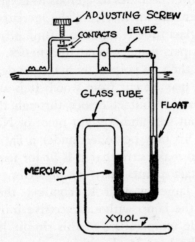

FIG. 47. The details of the automatic thermostat used with the incubator.

colors. As for the sealed end, a mere heating to the point of melting will take care of this.

The blind end of the tube is filled with xylol to the level indicated. This material is employed because of its very high coefficient of expansion. The mercury is poured in on this, and here care must be exercised. Mercury is difficult to handle, and it is as quick as lightning when it gets away. Being extremely heavy, it will run off any surface quickly unless that surface is perfectly level. It will also leak through very small holes, and its fumes are dangerous, the more so because they produce no odor. Therefore, if a great deal of mercury escapes and runs away into the crevices of floors, the continued occupation of the room thereafter becomes dangerous in no small measure. The best way of inserting the mercury into the end of the glass tube is to make a funnel from heavy wrapping paper, using several thicknesses. The mercury should then be poured with a great deal of care.

The float may be cut from wood. It is attached to the lever on the contact device through the agency of a small but stiff and straight piece of No. 18 copper wire. This may be rolled under a flat board on the bench to make sure that it is fit for use.

The contact points may be of silver, and they should be large enough to conduct the current needed for the lamp without excessive burning.

The inside temperature of this simple little incubator may be kept level within wide limits by the simple trick of adjusting the screw carrying the contact. A little experience will be needed, but a day or two should be sufficient to permit the operator to gain good control over inside conditions.

Index

147